To My Dear Wife
on Her Birthday
1988

Love
Reg
XXX

Front Cover Inset: *The Author pushing the tub found in Eldorado.*

Back Cover Inset: *The Author entering Smithy Level through a small shaft.*

The
Hidden Side of
Swaledale

This book is dedicated to the late Edward Allen MBE,
former Emeritus Professor of Economics at the
University of Durham, who in 1958/59 awakened in
me an interest in Economic History which never
abated and ultimately led to the completion of
this work.

ISBN 0 948 511 40 0

Surface Photography

Ronnie Mullin
Supported by
John and Peter Hardy

Underground Photography
John and Peter Hardy

Published by
Frank Peters Publishing Ltd.
Kendal, Cumbria

Printed by
Frank Peters Colour Printers
Kendal, Cumbria

Typeset by
Facsimile Typesetters
Kendal, Cumbria

Designed by
Ram Design Associates Ltd.
Kendal, Cumbria

The Hidden Side of Swaledale

The Life and Death of a Yorkshire Lead Mining Community

John Hardy

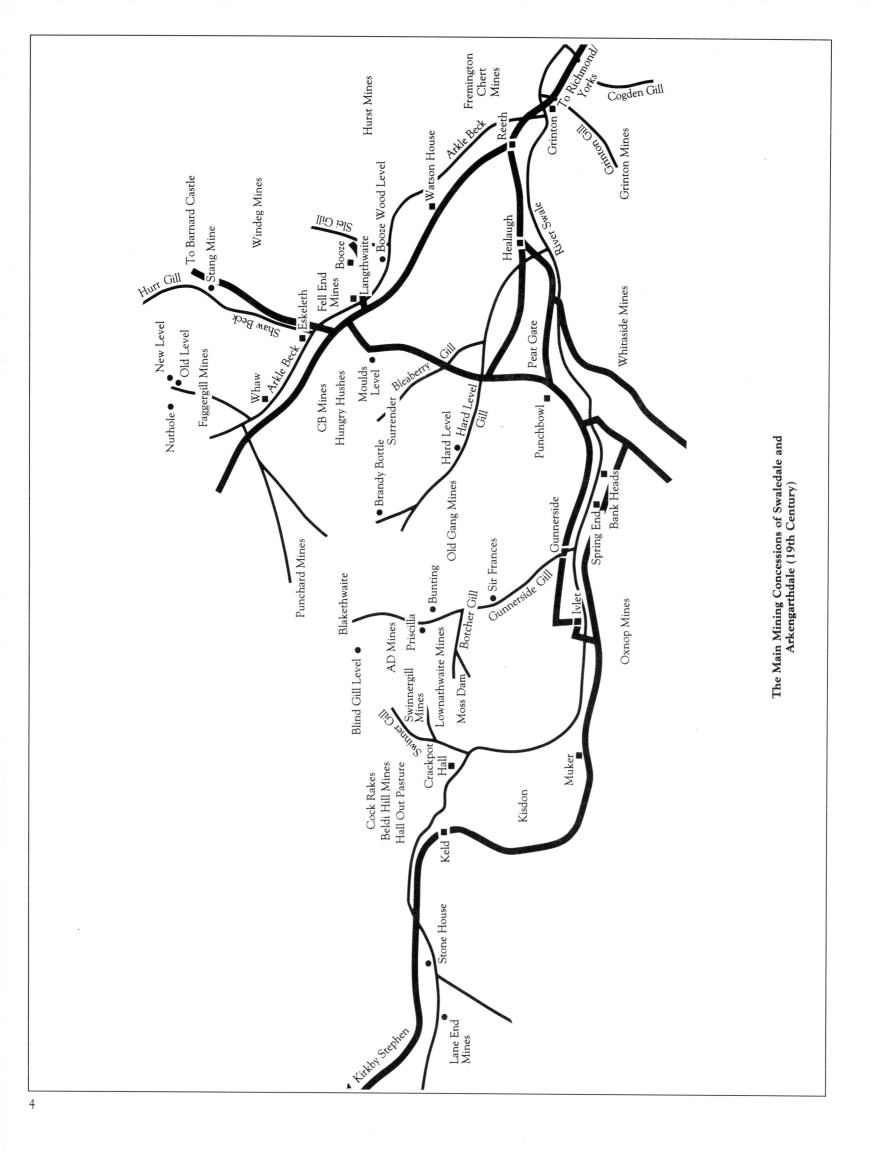

The Main Mining Concessions of Swaledale and Arkengarthdale (19th Century)

Contents

6

Photographs

Maps and Illustrations

Merryfield House, all that now remains of the old Clarkson family home.

Introduction

The 12th of May 1778 was a day never to be forgotten by James Clarkson. He was 26, a young miner in his prime living in the family home Merryfield House, located far out on the lonely moor directly adjacent to the Merryfield and Old Rake Veins in the Swaledale Orefield, which at this time appears to have been leased to the London Lead Company. So close is the house to the mines that it must have belonged to Lord Pomfret the mine owner and James therefore would have held some official position in the management hierarchy of the leasing company. The old stone house stood surrounded by mine workings, the Thompson and Shake Shafts being less than 200 yards away. Nearby was the quarry that supplied the stone supporting many a mine roof, ensuring the miner's safety.

James bade his young wife Alice and son farewell and made his way down toward the gill and Old Rake Whim. As he drew level with Moorhouse, he could just see a corner of Level House a half a mile away, formerly the home of Adam Barker a distinguished mine manager of 100 years earlier.

Later that day, word spread like wildfire in the dale that there had been a disaster at the Whim Shaft and anxious weeping women began to appear at the mine towards early evening. They were comforted by strained officials who urged on the rescuers as they tore at the rubble with their bare hands knowing that if they did not break through to the level soon enough the whole of the shift would be drowned, a thought too horrendous to be contemplated.

Work went on non stop through the night and 27 hours were to elapse before the broken lifeless bodies of brothers James Spensley of Smarber and Ralph Spensley of Blades were brought to the surface. The miners one by one escaped from the flooding level to fall into the arms of their loved ones, the fact that they were soaked to the skin and plastered with mud seemed not to be noticed. The tragedy of that day devastated Swaledale and a blanket of depression descended upon the community that immediately went into mourning.

This is a reconstruction of the events occurring on that fateful day based upon the evidence available. The deaths of the Spensleys are recorded in official documents, although my wife's grandmother made her own record providing the illuminating detail of the near demise of James Clarkson.

The fact that the Clarksons lived in the old stone house at Merryfield was transmitted to Harold Brown through James Kendall an old miner who worked on the Fryerfold Vein in the 19th Century. James Kendall died in 1922 when he was 71 and 60 years later Mr. Brown passed the information on to me.

The Clarksons clearly were closely associated with the Old Gang Mining Company for the mine map of 1861, now in my possession, was produced by James A. Clarkson of Arkengarthdale, the grandson of James Clarkson who so narrowly escaped death at Old Rake Whim. The map gives a remarkable confirmation of Mr. Brown's information for James A. Clarkson could not resist drawing in Merryfield House on the map that he was commissioned to produce.

Sir Francis Mine, Gunnerside Gill.

Before James Clarkson retired to Turnip House near Blades to become a farmer in 1807, his wife had born him eight children, seven of whom lived.

As one day I gazed at the lonely expanse that was Merryfield with only scars to suggest its former activity, I could barely imagine the piping voices of children at play, the activity at the quarry and shafts whilst carts lumbered on their way to the smelter. It was hard to believe that this now lonely and deserted place could have been so different 200 years earlier.

I first came to Swaledale in 1946 and returned as the young Methodist Minister in 1954. I did not realise then, that I was living in the last days of a people whose way of life which had endured for centuries was coming to an end. I gained a considerable affection for them and developed a fascination for their ancestors, the old lead miners. Along with a record of my mining research I have penned a sketch of the people amongst whom I lived and their way of life which is no more.

In 1956, I married into a dales family that could boast strong mining connections back to James Clarkson, my wife's great great great grandfather. About 100 years on from the tragedy at the Old Rake Whim the Clarkson family like so many others in Swaledale had to endure the pain of parting with loved ones who felt compelled to emigrate to America where they successfully made their mark.

Bunting Mine & the 3 Hushes Fryerfold, Bunting and Gorton.

One of the great difficulties that I discovered when finally I settled to grapple with the subject of this book, was that much of its substance had literally disappeared. Whilst in conversation with an old friend the late Mrs. Herring of Gunnerside who was then 92, she said of the male population of her childhood days, "They were all miners". She was born in 1888 just after the Old Gang Company had surrendered its lease in 1887 and now, 100 years later, the miners are all gone. It was this shock realisation that led me to the conclusion, that the nearest that I could now hope to come to them, was to examine the work of their hands in the mines themselves, to discern the nature of their activities.

Across the years, I have felt a strong compulsion to carry out my investigations, often doing so with great reluctance. The observations that I now make and the record of events presented is personal in nature deriving from a commitment to uncover some of the skills, techniques and activities of this now extinct body of men, who over a period of nearly 2000 years dug into the hills of Swaledale for lead ore.

I acknowledge an indebtedness to such people as Arthur Raistrick, Bernard Jennings, P. W. Crabtree and others. My intermittent wanderings might have come to little purpose but for certain happenings which changed the course of events. Some of the Old Gang Mine maps were presented to me by my wife's uncle Mr. Harold Brown, my brother joined me on my exploration trips entirely changing the horizon of possibilities and someone began to open up previously inaccessible mines.

A vote of thanks must go to my wife and sister-in-law who endured many uncertain hours whilst the mines were being explored. I gratefully acknowledge the help of the NCB through its employees at Littleton Colliery who kindly loaned me the lamps without which much of our work could not have been done. Finally I mention my blacksmith, upon whom we sometimes depended for our lives, who exercising skills like his ancestors before him, made many things possible.

The photographs presented have been taken with the most primitive equipment and often in the most appalling conditions. The fact that it worked at all in some environments is a tribute to those who made it and was a constant source of amazement. Our great enemy water, hindered us just as it had the miners before us. We constantly fought to protect our equipment, enduring repeated soakings for hours on end and their inevitable consequences.

The old levels that we explored were driven from 120 to 200 years before and had received no maintenance for 80 to 100 years. Notwithstanding, we have found stemples as good as the day they were put in and capable of holding the combined weight of two men.

A special mention must go to my brother Peter, who along with me shared the joys and miseries of the field work. Indeed, it must be said that without his enthusiastic participation, this work could not have been completed. Together we have watched the levels deteriorate and have undertaken our work with the constant knowledge of the risks involved. We felt those risks to be justified by the end pursued and it is hoped that this record will provide a reference for the future, by helping us to recall an age that has passed. For my part, I will remember the decaying levels and subterranean paths of the Hidden Side of Swaledale.

Relics of a bygone age.

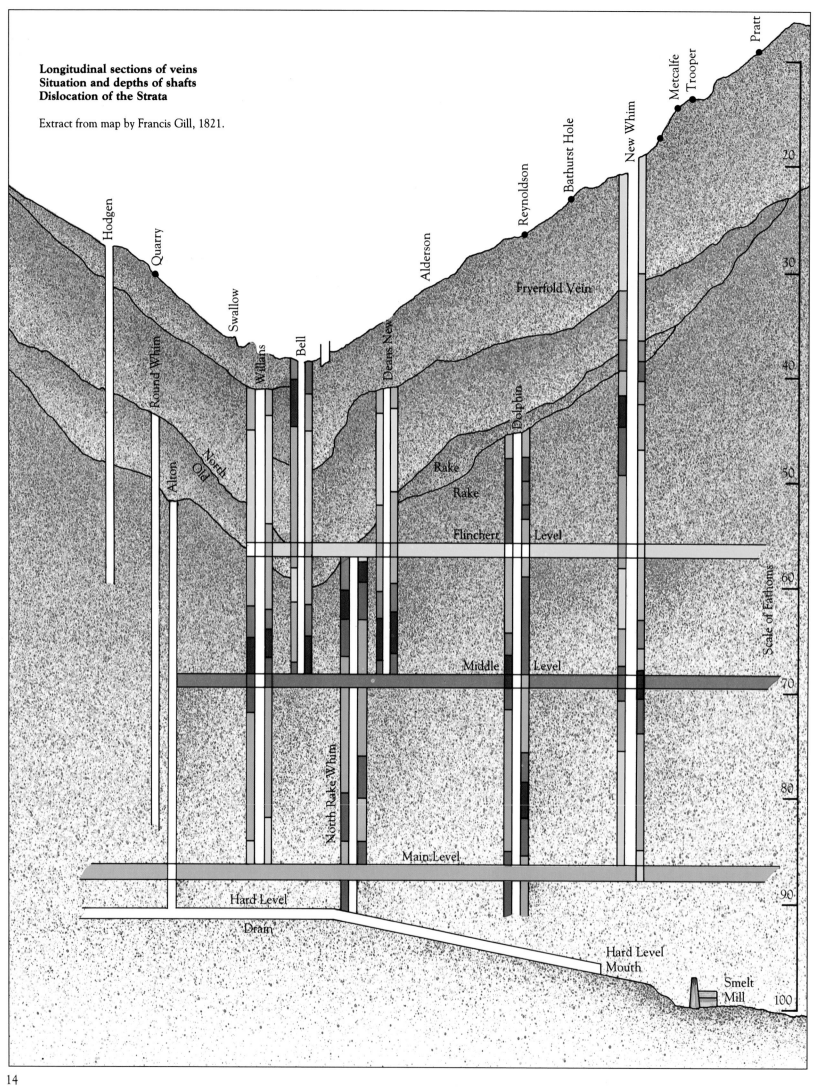

**Longitudinal sections of veins
Situation and depths of shafts
Dislocation of the Strata**

Extract from map by Francis Gill, 1821.

Pratt

Metcalfe
Trooper

New Whim

Bathurst Hole

Reynoldson

Alderson

Fryerfold Vein

Hodgen

Quarry

Swallow

Round Whim

Willans

Bell

Deans New

Alton

North

Old

Dolphin

Rake

Rake

Flinchert   Level

Middle   Level

North Rake Whim

Main Level

Hard Level

Dram

Hard Level
Mouth

Smelt
Mill

Scale of Fathoms

20

30

40

50

60

70

80

90

100

1

How the Mines Were Worked

The geology of Swaledale belongs to the Yoredale series with a regular pattern of limestones, shales and sandstones. Lead ore was located in faults, mainly in the upper limestones and chert beds along with other minerals like Baryte, Fluorite, Whitherite and Calcite. The miners would remove large amounts of these minerals along with the Galena, which they particularly sought. The unwanted minerals were dumped, since at the time there was no use for them. This however has now changed and the old dumps are being sifted through and useful minerals salvaged.

A vein may contain a good ore shoot that could either swell into a great mass or pinch out to nothing, leaving the miner to continue following it in the hope of reaching a productive strike. Sometimes a vein would only contain the gangue minerals with no lead, at others it might be barren and void of all mineral content, ensuring that mining would be speculative in nature.

Sir George Denys Bart noted that the main interest of the miners prior to his own time had been in the First or Main Limestone, the Black and Red Beds above and finally the Second or Underset Limestone. He was preoccupied with driving the Sir Francis Level to prove the Old Rake and Fryerfold Veins in the lower Fourth, Fifth and Sixth Limestones.

Initially, ore bearing veins were exposed by the erosion activity of the River Swale and its tributaries. Early mining took the form of an opencast operation called Hushing. Pliny the Roman Historian records that his kinsmen found the resident miners of Britain using this technique. Water was dammed at a convenient point, and when released, it swept away the topsoil exposing the vein. As it became increasingly difficult to work the surface, the miners, initially without the aid of gunpowder, began to sink shallow sumps or bell pits on to the vein. From these they bored lateral tunnels, called drifts, as far as they safely dare, for at this time there was no adequate provision for ventilation. With the aid of explosives, shafts got deeper and Jack Rollers used for haulage up short distances were replaced by the Whim Gin harnessed to a horse.

As mines went deeper so the problem of water dispersal became more critical. The answer to it was found under German influence in driving levels from the hillsides making access to the mines much easier as well as providing an easy method of drainage for water. Because of the hilly nature of Swaledale, levels made the use of large pumping engines less necessary, although at Lane End Mine in Upper Swaledale engines were needed, the ore bearing ground being so far beneath the river bed. They were not however entirely successful and in 1864, the A.D. Company commenced to drive the Catrake Level in an attempt to drain the mine but after 112 fathoms had been completed it was abandoned.

The miners' early tools consisted of a pick, drill and hammer. As shafts became deeper and technical problems increased the Gad appeared along with the Plug and Feathers. The Gad was driven into cracks and the Plug and Feathers were used in conjunction with it. Two wedges, the Feathers, would be driven into cracks and a third, the Plug was hammered between them. These methods, skilfully used, were capable of bursting rock. Another old mining practice was to light a charcoal fire against the forehead to heat up the rock which would then crack as it was drenched with water. The impact of such a working practice on the lungs hardly bears thinking about!

Ponderous methods of removing rock were finally superseded by the advent of gunpowder, which proved so successful for blasting purposes and was unrivalled until Sir George Denys Bart encouraged his miners to use dynamite late in the nineteenth century.

It is difficult to know when levels were first used in Swaledale, but a reference is made to an early one at Lownathwaite in 1701. Much later it was followed by such levels as Parkes, Swinnergill, Hard and Bunting, to name but a few.

The extract from Francis Gill's map of 1821 shows a section of the Old Rake, Fryerfold and North Rake Veins. It reveals the mine structure to consist of three principal levels, the Flintchert, Middle and Main Levels. The upper level gives access to the Chert Beds, whilst the Middle Level runs under the Black and Red Beds. The Main Level enabled lead ore deposits to be extracted from the Main Limestone which was largely inaccessible to earlier miners except in deep valleys because of its depth and the problem encountered with water. Yet further below still is the important Hard Level, driven to enable exploration of the Underset Limestone.

Old doorway in Priscilla Level.

The illustration of the section of the Fryerfold Vein in the region of Bell Shaft shows the Old Gang Mine to be more complex than hitherto described. The distance between the main levels are considerable, and in order to gain access to ore bearing ground it is often necessary to put in a rise or sink a sump from which a drift may be driven. Drifts are smaller than main levels which were constructed large enough to use horses for transport purposes. Transport in a drift, was usually obtained by the miner pushing a relatively small wooden tub rather than the eight to nine foot tubs used in the main levels. Prior to these developments, miners carried ore with the weight on their shoulders assisted by a halter, to which wooden buckets were attached, or children dragged buckets in small drifts strapped to them by means of a harness.

The Bell Shaft was used for several years to raise ore to the surface, which was then transported overground to the smelt mill. A main sump was in the same vicinity into which water drained from the various upper levels. It is not therefore altogether surprising to find the Black Cross Cut commencing nearby. It was a major feature of the Hard Level network, although located above it, and was expressly put in to carry away water from the Fryerfold Vein. To facilitate this end, a steam engine was installed by Frederick Hall in about 1815 and operated for at least a few years before it was withdrawn after he had left the Old Gang Mining Company.

Old rock laden platforms, Windeg Mine.

An important feature of a mine was a main rise which would be driven to connect main levels. These rises would help to unwater upper strata as well as provide a means of communication and improved ventilation. Small trial drifts would often lead off from these rises and provide access to any discovered ore bearing ground. Illustrations of the function of such rises are to be found between the Sir Francis, Priscilla and Blind Gill Levels on the Watersykes Veins.

The map of the Old Gang Mines shows something of its complex of veins, cross cuts, adits and some shafts. A cross cut is an important feature in a mine since it is used to connect the ore veins and hence provide communication for transport, air circulation and watering out purposes. The veins in Swaledale usually extend at an angle to the vertical although in one or two places like Oxnop Gill some horizontal veins or flats, caused by minerals replacing limestone, were discovered.

In working the veins, the miner preferred to rise upward. They put in stemples upon which they erected platforms. Unwanted rock was stacked on these platforms which enabled the miner to continue working up the vein. When he felt that the platform carried enough weight, he would construct another one. These constructions carrying tons of rock represent a considerable hazard, for as the beams rot they can no longer carry the great weight placed upon them and collapse, often blocking a level. As the miners followed the veins, it was inevitable that they would come upon the work of former generations of their kind and in this manner the miners and mines came to be spoken of as 'the Old Man'.

Where a sump is driven below the floor level and no adit is available a pumping engine is necessary to raise water from the workings as was the case in the Sir Francis Mine, where the now celebrated engine was erected to pump out the Tiplady Drift and the lower workings 130 feet below the rails.

After ore was brought to the surface, the process of separating the lead from other unwanted elements began. It was crushed to a small size, usually by boys or women wielding buckers, a hammer-like tool. It was then put through a sieving process prior to its despatch to the mill for smelting.

Later the water wheel and crushing equipment to break up the ore into small pieces was

Blakethwaite Smelt Mill.

introduced into the larger mines. The broken ore then had to be dressed, that is put through a sieving process which used the principle of specific gravity to separate the lead from the unwanted minerals. This process was greatly improved with the introduction of the Hotching Tub which in essence was nothing more than a large sieve.

The dressed ore was taken to the smelter where the sulphur was burned out of it with the result that the lead became malleable rather than brittle as it had been previously.

The smelted lead was placed in moulds which when full would be allowed to cool and hence become 'pigs'. These pigs of lead would be marked by the Company that produced them after which in the 18th. and 19th. Centuries they were transported by horse to Richmond, thence to Yarm and Stockton and finally by sea to London, Newcastle or the Continent.

The ruins of a considerable number of Smelt Mills are still to be found. They are Keld, Beldi Hill, Swinnergill, Blakethwaite, Grinton, Old Gang, Surrender, the High and Low Mills at Marske and the Octagon and New Mills of Arkengarthdale.

The extent of mining in the Swaledale field was such that the operations of different companies ran into one another and it was for this reason that in the late 19th Century it was possible to enter the Sir Francis Mine in Gunnerside Gill and travel through the vast underground network to emerge into daylight from the Moulds Level in Arkengarthdale, a distance of over 10,000 yards or 6 miles.

To make such a mammoth journey,* we would need to climb 300 feet up two rises from the Sir Francis through the George to Bunting Level bringing us to the Old Rake Vein at its junction with the Miller Cross Cut. About a half mile down the Old Rake, we would descend 24 feet from Bunting to Hard Level. We now journey through the Merrifield Mines, on past Moorhouse Vein to North Rake Vein Cross Cut. Turning North we locate North Rake Whim Shaft. Thirty feet up inside it is the Black Cross Cut which will take us to the Brandy Bottle Incline.

Half way up the incline we pick up the Brandy Bottle Vein and travel some 2200 yards right through the Sun Vein in both the Old Gang and Surrender concessions to meet the C.B. boundary. An alternative to the Black Cross Cut is to turn east along North Rake Vein, then north into Pedleys Cross Cut and climb the 54 feet rise from Hard Level into Top Level at its junction with South Vein.

Strangely, I have seen no Old Gang Map showing the link between North Rake Vein and Top Level in the Sun Vein. The Swaledale Mining Companies have a reputation for not completing all the details on their maps and this would be particularly so during their last years of operation. Perhaps Ralph Place gave a hint of the road when he recommended a trial in 1870 for the continuation of the Durk Drift in Brandy Bottle East.

The final lap of the journey takes us on along the Sun Vein in C.B. territory, then via a cross cut to the Stemple Vein, whence we descend the rise from the Moulds level and hence are able to emerge into daylight in Arkengarthdale.

*Refer pages 26, 70 & 71.

The Old Smithy Crackpot, Beldi Hill.

Longitudinal section of part of Fryerfold Vein. North view of levels and works.

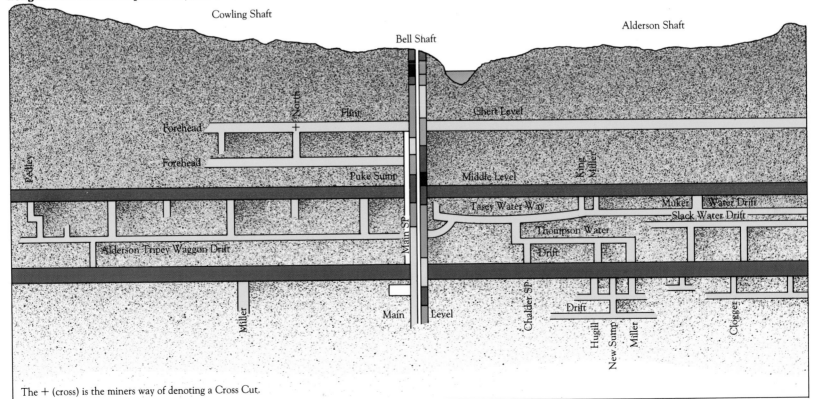

The + (cross) is the miners way of denoting a Cross Cut.

The derelict Crackpot Hall built by Lord Warton. This property was at the centre of the dispute between Lord of the Manor Thomas Smith and Lord Pomfret.

2

An Old Battleground

It was a clear day, the sun was shining and snow had fallen on the moor tops as I looked from Cock Rakes at the breathtakingly beautiful view commanded by the now derelict Crackpot Hall. I found it hard to believe that this now deserted landscape, where the casual walker hears only the plaintive cry of the Pewit protecting her young and the chunner of the Grouse scurrying for cover, was the scene of so much bitter conflict during the mid eighteenth century.

These events have been well documented and concerned the miners in the service of the Wharton Estate at Swinnergill and those working for Parkes and Company, Beldi Hill Mines. The Parkes brothers had taken a lease from Thomas Smith, who had purchased Crackpot Hall and its outpasture from the Wharton Trustees in 1738 who at the time of the transaction reserved all mineral rights in the common land.

Old abandoned tub at the mouth of Swinnergill Level.

Relations between the two mining groups took a decided turn for the worse when the Beldi Hill Company denied the use of the Parkes Level, driven between 1746/49, to the Wharton Estate. When it ceased to have any further value for Parkes and Company they requested some consideration from the Wharton Estate since it drained some of their shafts to the East of Swinnergill. Taking a rather high handed attitude to the smaller company the Trustees refused their request, a decision that was to have repercussions far beyond their wildest dreams.

Doubtless enraged by the unreasonable attitude adopted by the larger mining concern across the beck the Parkes brothers sealed and flooded their level. In doing so they also flooded some of the Swinnergill workings and this necessitated the driving of the Swinnergill Level in 1752.

The great dispute arose when Parkes and Company sublet a mining concession in 1767 to Richard Metcalfe of Calvert Houses and his partner John Scott in Hall Out Pasture. George Fermor, the second Lord Pomfret gained possession of the Wharton Estate through his marriage to Anna Maria Draycot in 1764. He contended that only he could grant leases on the land in question, whereas Thomas Smith, owner of Crackpot Hall, affirmed that it had, as long as anyone could remember, been a recognised part of Crackpot farm land. Great bitterness was engendered between the two companies and the miners, never easily controlled, expressed their allegiance in overt fashion. Pomfret's men sank shafts on Metcalfe land and put in cross cuts to the vein. At one point they burst into their opponents' workings and drove them out by violence. Water was turned down a shaft and it was during this incident that David Brunskill defending the Beldi Hill interest was thrown contemptuously into the hush gutter. Spout Gill Smelt Mill at Oxnop changed hands several times to the accompaniment of 'fisty cuffs' and Pomfret's men seized the ore there. Fearing that the mine might be raided, Metcalfe and Scott moved 520 tons of ore to various locations.

The litigation in respect of the dispute dragged on for many years, but judgement was finally given for Smith of Crackpot Hall, who received £400 by way of compensation for the damage caused to his property. Lord Pomfret, however, who had overburdened himself with debt, was finally committed to the Tower of London.

It is a matter of some surprise that miners who lived in such poor circumstances could identify so completely with Lord Pomfret. In these times however, class divisions were very distinct, although not dwelt upon, and the upper classes were conceived as bearing responsibilities as well as possessing privileges. More importantly, the fortunes of His Lordship would have a direct economic impact upon his charges, and against such a background the events that took place on Beldi Hill become completely understandable.

In less turbulent times in 1846, James Kearton and twenty associates made a bargain with the Beldi Hill Company to work the Oldfield Hush, and did so productively for 16 years. They made two dams and successfully used them to promote their work.

The ancestors of the waring miners to whom I ministered numbered among them many loyal Methodists who would emerge from their remote farms regularly for Sunday worship. To visit these people was an education to one who had been born amidst the urban sprawl. Long walks across rough moorland tracks would end with a pressing invitation to partake of their hospitality.

About two and a half miles upstream from Keld, a short distance from the Old Lane End Mine stands Stone House. It was the home of the Aldersons, a strongly committed Christian family.

Shaft in Swinnergill Mine.

Some of the chicks had fled the nest and Mrs. Alderson, now a widow, lived there with her two farming sons, Jim and Albert. I was overwhelmed by the sheer magnificence of the Swale roaring past the house, where I partook of the warm hospitality offered within its walls.

Jim was a tall thoughtful man and not long after my visit to Stone House he acquired the Cathole Inn which he renamed Hope House. The fact that he had no plans to continue the use of the property as a licensed premise occasioned some criticism and the story made some of the National Daily Newspapers at the time.

After he took up residence in Keld we struck up a warm friendship. I well remember visiting him one night when the snow was piled against his door. Inside was a roaring warm fire and he introduced me to a litter of small piglets that he was rearing in a barrel sheltered from the wild storms outside. I was feeling particularly lonely and desolate at this time and he proved a great source of help to me.

During my meanderings in the Keld area, I entered several of the Beldi Hill Mines. I remember climbing with my son into a magnificent ore working that wandered off in many directions in the Landy Level. Crackpot Level, also called Top Level, was driven in the second half of the eighteenth century. It is very low and after several fathoms one passes the rise connecting it with Landy Level below. Deeper on into the mine, there is a most peculiar feature; a small narrow entrance going away to the right through which one could barely squeeze. Driven through shale it was in poor condition and could have led on to a shaft. I recalled how the Pomfret miners had burst into Beldi Hill workings, driving out the miners there, and wondered if this feature could have had any connection with this incident. It is difficult to know how any useful purpose could be served by an entrance that would barely accommodate a man.

Yet further in still, it was necessary to wade through water over knee height until a rise on to a stope in the Sun Vein is reached. The most notable feature of this section is the beautiful stalactites that hang from the roof and the large streaks of blue and red on the wall betraying the presence of copper and iron deposits.

Much further down the hill is the Low or Platehole Level and close to this mine is the impressive remains of a large dressing floor. It is necessary to penetrate a quarter of a mile into it to reach the vein, but when the old miners got there we understand they found little lead to reward their endeavours. Where the level divides, deeply embedded in the right hand wall was an old rock drill. To the left is a significant run-in that blocks any further progress. I reflected that it was here in 1882 that S. Raw fled, pushing a tub containing a younger companion, James Allinson, with flood water in hot pursuit. They had unwittingly blasted their way into old flooded workings in Landy Level and had to flee for their lives. By the time they had almost reached daylight the water was halfway up the level and the mine was never worked again after this event.

Narrow entry Crackpot level.

Swinnergill Mine.

For a considerable period of time, I was of the opinion that it was not possible to enter the Swinnergill Mines. The Main Level was clearly visible, but I wrongly concluded that it was a watercourse connected to the old smelt mill nearby and never investigated it. One day, chancing upon a large crack in the rock structure near to the level entrance, I climbed through it and found myself peering into the gloom of Swinnergill Mine which in those days was partly blocked by a large iron tub laid on its side. Later emerging from the mine's dank and cold interior that day, I sat contemplating the crystal waters as they tumbled over the fall on their way out of East Grain. It was a beautiful day and as the warm air thawed my chilled flesh, the place seemed like paradise itself. Only grudgingly could I bring myself to leave what to me had become 'God's Acre'.

Semi Arch, Swinnergill Level.

Some 50 yards into Swinnergill Level it divides, passageways leading to right and left going on to the Sun, Middle and North Veins. At the junction of these roadways, there is a shaft and a strong stream of water between the rails of the left passage disappears into it. This powerful flow of water, despite my expectations to the contrary, showed no sign of diminishing in volume during the drought of 1976. There is little doubt that this shaft connects with Parkes Level across the beck which was reopened in 1873 by the AD Company, but was abandoned five years later when it was discovered that the veins were not productive enough at this depth. Across the years, neglect has led to the build up of about three and a half feet of sludge in the level, making it virtually inaccessible. It was the blocking of this waterway that led to so much ill feeling and helped to fuel the flames of the previously mentioned great dispute between the two mining companies in the eighteenth century.

The left hand of the two passageways in Swinnergill Mine is much smaller than the other and has proved less interesting. The right hand level gives access to several rises onto large stopes, and timbers positioned a hundred or more years ago are still visible. Just as I was entering the level in 1980, and noting that the old iron tub had been removed, I heard a loud crash as something fell. I expected to find some evidence of what had been heard, but to my surprise never did. The masons' archways had withstood the hammer-like blows of the falling debris. The removal of the old tub would have required much enterprise and energy. I remember weighing up the possibilities of salvage and finding it beyond my capabilities. It would have been difficult to get it upright in the mine apart from anything else, for the roof was so low there, but to further bring it over the moor would have presented enormous problems.

Many fathoms into the mine, above the level and to its left, there was an open shaft stretching away to the surface down which water gently tumbled. I took a compass bearing here, 82 degrees East, and found it on the surface behind the old Swinnergill Smelt Mill. It had been skilfully lined with limestone blocks and measured 70 feet to the floor. It appeared to be acting as an airshaft.

There was some particularly fine arching in this mine, and I reflected that it was a pity that such outstanding examples of the skill of masonry would be permanently hidden from view. After what seemed an age my way was barred, although with a difference. It is usual for run-ins from rises to block the way ahead, but not so on this occasion. The level was pressed in, and stone work displaced. With the greatest difficulty I managed to squeeze through the gap, only to find myself confronted by a long section of level that had been subject to intense earth movements, and it was not possible to go any further.

About 400 yards up the beck beyond Swinnergill Kirk, reputed to be an old place of worship in a time of religious persecution, there is an old adit driven into the shale beside a waterforce. It is about four feet in height and was probably an eighteenth century mine. Inside the mining was carried out by means of sumps which are now completely filled with water, burying what must have been sizeable workings.

During one beautiful summer afternoon, I carried out an investigation of the Oldfield Hush Gutter. It was not difficult to trace the arrangements as they were in the time of James Kearton and associates. I remember being trapped on the north wall of the hush gutter for some ten minutes. A wrong move there could cost a man his life, and I hoped fervently that the miners of old had chosen some other place than here to throw David Brunskill into the hush gutter. The site of the dams is still visible and the pit used to trap the ore at the foot of the hush, although completely filled with large rocks and scarcely recognisable, can be found.

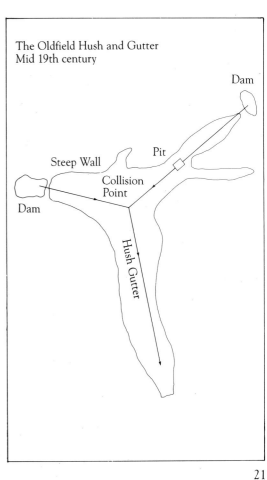

The Oldfield Hush and Gutter
Mid 19th century

Dam

Pit

Steep Wall

Collision
Point

Dam

Hush Gutter

Looking at the layout of the hush gutter, it is clear than one source of water would be arranged to collide with the other, to ensure that it would quickly make its way down the gutter to the River Swale.

This beautiful and lonely place is now presided over by decaying remnants of old buildings and works that once throbbed with life. On one of these in the Pomfret Denys royalty I saw the date 1902 inscribed, and near to it the name of J. Sunter chiselled on the stone. At this time the mines were already a spent force and destined never to revive. If these broken shells could but talk, what tales of loyalty and violence would they tell? But time has swept the board clean, and man no longer reigns here. The old battleground is deserted, for the passions of men have spent their force.

Old Gang Smelt Mill.

3

The Hard Level

Hard Level was driven whilst Lord Pomfret was in direct control of the Old Gang Mines. There is some confusion as to the date of its commencement but the evidence that I possess convinces me that it was about 1780, a date that bears some significance. First called Force Level after a nearby waterfall, it soon became evident that the going was to be hard and hence it became known as the Hard Level.

The cross cut to the vein was intended to come in under the Underset Limestone. It was 1150 yards from the level mouth to the vein and we are led to understand that it cost an average of £5 per yard to complete.

The direction taken by the level is most intriguing, travelling for about 620 yards close to the line of the beck in a NNW direction after which it switches for the remainder of its course toward the North. The question that immediately arises is, why did Lord Pomfret not take the shortest route (a) to the vein? (see below). Such a course would have had some advantage for it would have saved a drive of some 50-60 yards. Routes (b) and (c) are recorded on James A. Clarkson's map, suggesting that (b) was the one finally approved whilst (c) is the level's actual course, its twists and turns betraying the hardships endured by those who drove if forward. Yet another question to be answered is, how can the long drive of 620 yards to the NNW be justified? Only, I suggest, if the level was intended to follow route (d) which comes in just west of Hill Top Whim if followed through. Could the near total disaster of 1778 have finally convinced Lord Pomfret of the need for a lower level to drain his mines? Doubtless the economic need for such a trial had often been argued thoroughly but the risks involved in finally finding little reward at the end of such a costly venture was a powerful disincentive for starting it. The accident of 1778 was the type of event that could overcome the natural reluctance to take a risk. It must be born in mind that at this time the mines were in isolated pockets and the process of joining them up was mainly completed in the following 50-60 years.

Hill Top Whim is 350 yards west of Hard Level Head. On the surface it is located up the bank behind the ruins of Level House. Its position betrays its former importance, being close to an official's house, hard by a smithy where miners would collect their drills before descending the shaft and adjacent to the road, thus giving good access to the smelt mill.

Alice Clarkson said that the accident of 1778 took place at Old Rake Whim. In 1861 James Clarkson records three whim shafts on his map along the Old Rake Vein. They are Alton, Hill Top and Dolphin. Earlier in 1821 Francis Gill ignores Hill Top but records the other two along with the Bell and Willan Shafts which we know were then currently in use. Alton and Dolphin were clearly named after persons and hence would be less likely to suffer a name change. Hill Top, however, expressing a geographical location, could easily be displaced by the miners to become Old Rake Whim. It would have been difficult for Gill to include Hill Top on his map, since it is about the same distance from Hard Level Gill as Bell and the one would overlay the other, moreover Bell was the more important at the time. Hill Top, however, must at least have had a ventilation function in the 19th Century. There is some good reason why James Clarkson includes it on his map. It could be conjectured that a man who felt the need to put the old family home upon his drawing, a seemingly pointless gesture, might just as easily feel compelled to include the whim shaft where his forebear nearly lost his life. That Hill Top and Old Rake Whim are one and the same seems a reasonable identification.

Lord Pomfret, the main driving force behind the completion of Hard Level, was a man of considerable influence, possessing estates and mining interests in both Cumberland and Yorkshire. Was it arrogance and the lure of wealth that encouraged him to engage in the bitter and damaging dispute with Thomas Smith, culminating in three appeals in two years to the House of Lords and his final incarceration in the Tower of London as a debtor?

Although this particular aspect of his life has captured the interest, it has been recognised that he made valuable contributions toward the fairer administration of the mines, particularly in discontinuing the Bing Tale system which enabled agents to act shamefully in bestowing favour toward friends and relatives. Lord Pomfret called for the ore that was presented to the lessors to be

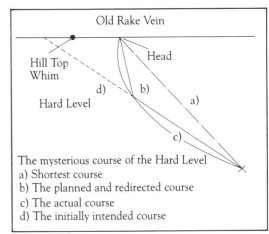

The mysterious course of the Hard Level
a) Shortest course
b) The planned and redirected course
c) The actual course
d) The initially intended course

properly dressed and fit for the market, so that all would be paid the same price for their work.

He was no absentee landlord, making frequent visits to the mines for the purpose of which in 1792 along with his son-in-law Peter Denys he acquired AD Hall, later renamed Draycot Hall.

He took what in his day was the bold decision to drive Hard Level. It may have been the case that there was a humanitarian element influencing his thinking in these matters. If this was the case, it shows a remarkable degree of concern for the miners on his part over 60 years before any mining legislation was enacted by Parliament. Economic factors, however, doubtless carried the greatest weight.

He had to bear the long barren years and mounting disillusionment as costs escalated and, unlike Sir George Denys Bart, he was unable to call advance technology to his aid. It is possible to gauge the progress of the level by reference to the traditional techniques used in the driving of the Sir Francis Mine up to 1870. A figure of 75 yards per annum is a reasonable estimate, which would mean that the Hard Level was 15 years before it reached Old Rake Vein. Were it to have continued on route (d), it would have taken more like 17 years. Whereas many another would have given up, Lord Pomfret kept his miners going. Heavily in debt, he would be under strong pressure to turn the level to make productive ground as soon as possible. It is noticeable that the roof of the level as it turns north is lower than that preceding it. Could Lord Pomfret's debts help to explain the rather strange course of Hard Level and along with its diminished size be giving mute testimony to an original intention that was frustrated?

His faith and determination were rewarded with mines equipped to take advantage of the high prices offered for lead as they rocketed above £30 per ton at the turn of the nineteenth century during the Napoleonic Wars. The lead output of Lord Pomfret's mines rose from 583 tons in 1790 to an average of 2,000 tons in the first decade of the nineteenth century.

Having no male heir, his earldom died with him as he was unable to persuade George IV to offer more than a baronetcy to Peter Denys, who though refusing the honour himself, secured it for his son George William, father of the more noted Sir George who emanated his great grandfather Lord Pomfret when he drove the Sir Francis level.

The same determination and drive that prolonged the tedious Beldi Hill dispute that so nearly destroyed him, fired Lord Pomfret in the opening of levels that were to ensure the operation of his mines for another 100 years.

He had emerged from the disgrace of the Tower to rehabilitate the family name and fortune. Just as the names of Sir George and Sir Francis Level are inexorably linked, so too must the names of Lord Pomfret and Hard Level.

My first visit to the Hard Level took place in the early 1960's. The water in the first 300 yards lay at somewhere above knee height. I rather fearfully made my way in it until confronted with a blockage, and was rather happy to make a hasty retreat. Several years later I was back again along with my brother and by now the water level was at chest height. The stoppage had not been caused as I originally thought by a natural fall. At this point in the mine, the Hard Level was beneath a shaft, access to which used to be gained further up the beck. It was conveniently used to supply the level with air. At some stage miners had used the rise as a convenient dump for their 'deads' (unwanted rock), thus blocking the Hard Level.

A significant clearance had been made to permit a man to crawl through the debris before us. I did so in order to take a photograph after which I fully intended to leave the mine. My brother's curiosity, however, was clearly getting the better of him. We were sitting in a small chamber and could see the level going on at the other side of it. The water before us seemed somewhat forbidding but after sufficient prodding, I felt emboldened to test it for depth, and before long we were pressing on up the level. It was in this rather uncertain manner that a key was inserted into the door of an Aladdin's cave which we relentlessly explored for the next few years. We had crossed our Rubicon.

The chest high water soon fell away and we were racing between the rails which were still in all the way to Hard Level Head. One marvelled that the miners of old had managed to drive this long level with their simple rock drills, hammers and black powder. It seemed a remarkable feat for a trial of this magnitude to be embarked upon, which must have tried their patience as year after year they hacked out rock with no immediate hope of reaching the vein. Our trek seemed endless and we came to yet another fall, but the water build-up here was not serious. Eventually, my attention was drawn to a working in the right hand wall. I remember saying, "We are on the vein, the Head must be just up front", and sure enough it was.

It was a moment of great significance for me to be in this place, where the mine branched away in three directions. The vein was massive here, being six to seven feet wide and contained a stick of dynamite that had never fired. With my imagination, I wondered at the many meetings and conversations that had taken place here by successive generations of miners. Our success of this day had changed the character of our activities. Up to this time we had prodded on the fringes of the subject of study, but now we were at the heart of a great mine. Subjects of enormous interest

beckoned our attention and from now on, metaphorically speaking, we were no longer to probe the foothills, but rather accept the challenge to more Everest-like endeavours. A continuing feature of our work, was the enlarging of its scope. In the end we felt that we had seen enough to understand how the Old Man had carried through his purpose.

Before us was Whites Cross Cut, which extended for 300 yards on to the eastern end of North Rake Vein. The rails were still in, and at the end of it there was a rise going on to ore bearing ground above. Spoil had fallen from the rise and there was the inevitable build-up of water behind it. On a subsequent occasion, we investigated the North Rake. The water lay at about waist height in the level. Some 50 feet along it, Pedleys Cross Cut to the Sun Vein in the forefield branched away. The level in the vein here had completely collapsed and water was pouring in. Pedleys Cross Cut had been driven in the shale and not surprisingly was subject to many a fall. We were able to wade about one third of its length before it too had collapsed in and become impassable.

Some 25 yards into Whites Cross Cut, in the left hand wall, there is a rise close to a small vein. Our map told us that it drove up under Dolphins Whim which was used to lift ore to the surface before the more convenient levels were cut. We made several attempts to climb this rise but in the end we had to concede that the operation was unsafe because of the unstable silt that had fallen.

From the Head walking west up the vein there is much evidence of mining activity above the level. I recorded on our first visit, that we saw on the left hand side of the level what appeared to be a stope containing a rudimentary ladder. Subsequently, I understood that we were looking at a rise incorporating a hopper.

The use of the hopper in the Swaledale mines raises an interesting question. From the evidence available to us, the hopper was certainly in use toward the latter part of the eighteenth century and doubtless much earlier, although it is clear that they were not always used in the ore working process. There are many pointers in the mines to indicate that the miners often directly worked along a vein without using a hopper. On other occasions, however, the hopper was used and the question is, what was the guiding factor which determined whether such a technique was to be used or not? I think the answer to the question inevitably turned on the amount of material available. If ore bearing ground was serviced by a drift, then a hopper would be justified. Similarly, a very large ore body might prompt the building of its own exclusive hopper.

Travelling in an easterly direction down the Old Rake, we had hoped to gain access to the New, Reformer and Raw Veins. Our objective, however, was frustrated by a huge fall out that totally blocked the level a few fathoms from the head.

One of our unspoken aspirations was to complete the 'grand slam', that is to journey via the Brandy Bottle Incline and Black Cross Cut, through the network to emerge from the mine at Hard Level Gill. On the day set aside, we shrank from the undertaking, but somehow felt that it had to be done. Grimly determined, we plunged into the bitter waters of the Black Cross Cut, strangely not feeling the cold. Whilst we carried out this exercise we continued our investigations in the Hard Level. As we emerged from North Rake Vein Cross Cut, we were able to walk 115 yards along Old Rake Vein in a westerly direction before being halted by a run-in. A broadgauge railway was still in evidence and there were two significant workings, both run-in to the south of the level, serviced by broadgauge railway. The first was about 30 yards west of North Rake Vein Cross Cut. The fallen debris may well have concealed both overhead and sump workings. The Old Rake Vein was clearly to be seen in the roof, and the walls were covered by a beautiful white limestone. Returning to the cross cut, we moved down the Old Rake in an easterly direction into unknown conditions. There was a man-made obstruction in the level, and tension built up within us. Our fears were groundless, soon we could hear the gurgle of water and shortly after see the obstruction which began to force us up toward the roof. We ended up inching our way forward on our stomachs in four inches of water. After about 50 feet we could begin to stand again and not long hence had reached familiar ground.

Refreshing ourselves at Hard Level Head, we finally moved off down the level. We were apprehensive, since we had not travelled this way for two years. We suppressed the fear that we might have to face the misery of returning from whence we had come, a daunting prospect, since we had consumed all our hot drinks.

At the Head end of the level, the last 350 yards is lower than the rest, making travelling difficult. In this section the sound of helmets striking against the roof is commonplace and moving forward in a bent posture inevitably leads to bouts of backache.

In the right of the level about 300 yards from the Head, we passed a working in the wall that rose about 8-10 feet and then proceeded in the form of an incline. We pondered this trial which we thought at first was an unfinished air shaft. Later, however, we could see that it was following a vein which had remained very thin and hence was abandoned by the miners. This same vein was probably worked above in Wiseman's Level. About 300 yards further on down Hard Level we are close to the Spence Level and Healaughside Vein. It carries the dubious distinction of being the site of the last fatality in the Old Gang Mines on January 29th, 1926. Mining operations at the time

Inspecting the Rise under Dolphins Whim.

Stone arch supported by rock drills.

Fine piece of stone arching at North Rake Vein Cross Cut.

were apparently under the control of a certain Captain Vickers, who domiciled at the Buck Hotel. Joseph Sunter, a native dalesman, joined Benny Jones and Archie Rule, miners who had drifted north with the collapse of tin mining in Cornwall, in the hope of successfully exploiting a part of the Old Gang network. Joseph had taken an untried horse into the level for haulage purposes and something happened to startle it, whereupon it bolted, crushing poor Joseph beneath the tubs. It was late when they brought his body from the mine, and Dr. Spiers, the legendary doctor of the dale, decided that it would not be possible to reach his home on Whitaside before nightfall. He asked the licensee of the Punchbowl at Low Row to receive the body, but his request was refused. Dr. Spiers left and later returned with a constable demanding admittance with the body. As my informant put it, Dr. Spiers knew the law, the inn keeper did not.

We felt an immense sense of relief on that day on seeing that we could climb through the small hole at the air shaft, finally emerging from the mine into Hard Level Gill to experience a gloriously warm sunny evening in Swaledale after a six hour journey.

During one expedition to the mine it yielded up a hitherto closely guarded secret. Some 80 yards along the vein beyond the old rise previously mentioned and in the opposite wall, there was what we had always identified as an ore working. The wall of the level was a vivid red suggesting the presence of iron. This was an occasion of intense flooding, and we were amazed to discover a massive volume of water disgorging from what on previous occasions had been a relatively dry working. The quantity of water was so great, that we were led to conclude that it was draining from the Main Level above. We climbed into this stope and discovered that the miners had driven through black beds exposing a small area of limestone which was acting as a Puke Sump allowing water to escape through the cracks in the rock's structure. The vein had turned over toward the north, and water was entering the stope, 20 feet north of Hard Level, 50 feet above it.

Old Gang Mines

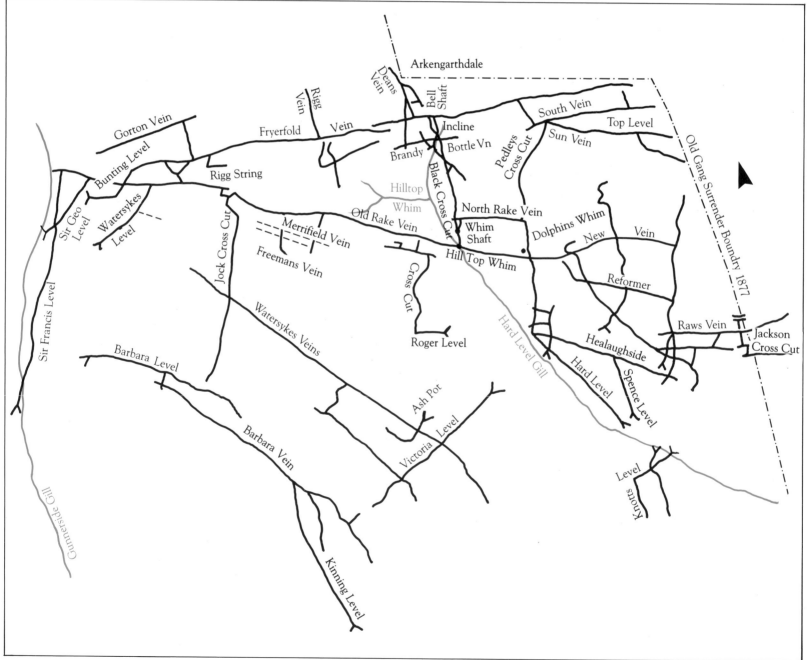

Considering the length of the cross cut to the vein, I was astonished at the poor provision made for ventilation. What there is, appears to have been supplied by the shaft located 300 yards into the mine and at the rise under Dolphins Whim at 1175 yards, which as previously mentioned is 25 yards into Whites Cross Cut. Sir George Denys Bart reckoned that ventilation rises were needed at 80 fathom intervals when a level was cut with hand labour. This is an interesting observation relative to the Hard Level since by Sir George's standards there would have been five rises between the old air shaft and Dolphins Whim. This comparison gives a good indication of the improvement of safety and health standards in 100 years.

Any miner participating in the opening out of this level would have a very hard bargain indeed. Driving forward year after year in the unyielding rock was bad enough, but to this we must add the permanent stench of gunpowder, an atmosphere laden with dust combined with a dangerous shortage of oxygen which was repeatedly blasted away from the forehead.

The driving of this level was an epic of human endurance and courage, a pointer to generations unborn. It was not a small matter for an officially named level to have that name changed with the obvious consent of the owners. I have already referred to the stringent times being faced by Lord Pomfret. To this we must add the fearful privations endured by the miners. Little wonder that by common consent, Force Level became Hard Level, completed because Lord Pomfret risked his capital and reputation whilst the miners put their health in jeopardy. It is not difficult to believe that they would be prime candidates for the dreaded miners' complaint, a lung disease that made them old men at the age of fifty if they had not already succumbed and found an early grave. It was a Hard Level indeed!

Cringley Hall.

Bunting Mine.

4

A Tale of Two Levels

For anyone who has entered a Swaledale level, it would be difficult for them to understand how it was that we could come to regard Bunting as a friendly level, but that is just how my brother and I came to think of it. It is virtually impossible not to notice it, standing as it does to the east of Gunnerside Gill, brooding over what was once a very extensive mining complex and set against the impressive backcloth of the three great hushes, Bunting, Fryerfold and Gorton.

The level was probably first driven under Bunting Hush in the late eighteenth century during the period of Lord Pomfret's stewardship, and it is evident that it was very productive. From 1802 for 20 years, John Davis was the agent for the Pomfret Denys Mines and history's recollection of him is not particularly flattering. Until Frederick Hall took over, he was also agent for the Aldersons at Old Gang Mine. The difference between these two men was as that between chalk and cheese and their dislike of each other was total. Employed as he was at a time when Lord Pomfret through age was probably taking a less active part in the management of his mining interests, one doubts that his lordship would have tolerated such an incompetent in his earlier years. His poor performance was protected to some degree by the high price being offered for lead during his period of management, but even then between 1811-14 he presented the Aldersons who had taken over Old Gang Mines with an enormous £20,000 loss over three years for which he was promptly dismissed.

The Author at the entrance to Bunting Mine.

He is remembered as something of a rogue and failed to distinguish himself in matters relating to mine management. Under his direction, Bunting Level was driven to connect with Hard Level in the Old Gang, but due to faulty surveying he allowed it to rise too quickly, and instead of Bunting making a junction with Hard Level, it came in four fathoms above it, and had to be connected by means of a hopper. Even worse, this premature rising meant that a level which was designed to work the ore under the Second Limestone now had much of the lode beneath the tramlines.

From our point of view, however, we have often had occasion to reflect that Bunting Level is as sound as any in Swaledale. We probably gained some affection for it because we could carry out our work there at least in comparatively dry conditions and were not forever banging our heads upon the roof.

The level runs directly under the hush for 145 yards and its entrance was originally shrouded by a building. The remains of rich ore workings are to be found on either side of the level, and some 50 yards into it on the right hand side there is an interesting drift still containing a small gauge wooden railway.

After 145 yards, the level branches away sharply to the left into the Miller Cross cut. There is evidence of a vein in the wall here which ascends into a hopper above the rails. This hopper proved a great source of information and will be mentioned elsewhere. After 330 yards from the entrance the level swings away to the right following the Old Rake Vein, whilst Miller Cross Cut continues on for another 50 yards before it cuts the Fryerfold Vein. From this point for nearly 300 yards, there is now very little of interest to be seen apart from a place where the miners supported the level with rock drills. The apparent absence of ore bearing ground here did cause me to wonder how the miners had ever made a living.

At first, I had imagined that stone arching was only used to support a level as it was passing through poor rock. The truth is, of course, that the very extensive use of arching in this section of the mine was concealing the mine workings above my head, and also providing strong resistance to falling debris.

Eventually collapsed workings had partly blocked the level and progress from here was in waist high water. The next feature of interest was Taylor's Rise located in the right hand wall of the mine. After a few yards the level swung sharply to the left and soon we were faced with a partial blockage. I remembered having seen this before on a previous visit, and had used it as a convenient pretext for turning back, but there would be no turning back again. After squeezing through the narrow opening, we soon came into the dry. After seeing some signs of activity in the left hand wall, we were next confronted by an old hopper perched directly above the rails. We were now 950 yards into the mine at Rigg String. Everything was walled in, and only blocked access points through walls were visible apart from the hopper mouth protruding through the roof of the mason's arch.

At about 1,500 yards our progress was halted by a massive fall out in the region of Rigg Vein and the Fryerfold Shaft. Above our heads we could see the vein pinching out. There had been rails all the way from the level entrance and no sign of it having got above the main ore body, as it had done so disastrously in the Old Rake. The forehead of Bunting in the Fryerfold Vein reached 308 fathoms beyond Rigg Vein in 1848 and I have no knowledge as to whether it went any further. It came in under the Main Level which joins up with Deans Vein and the Brandy Bottle Incline.

When I first visited Bunting, the Old Rake Vein was completely inaccessible after a few yards. However, someone with mining skills later punched a hole through the run in, and we were able to squeeze through and continue on up the level for some 200 yards.

The Sir Francis Engines Inlet Pipe as seen from deep inside Staple Shaft.

We quickly entered dry ground and saw evidence, perhaps pointing to the faulty surveying that had taken place in the time of Davis. At first we were gingerly picking our way over a hole under the rails, and some 50 yards later we found that the rails had been ripped out, and we were gazing into a gaping hole 20 feet deep. There was a narrow iron ladder extending down into the hole, and this was obviously intended to assist anyone who wanted to go on into the mine and was probably used by the people who had dug out the floor. Above the hole there was a piece of fine stone arching, and a few yards on down the level a run in blocked further progress. The miners appeared to have cut an ore body, and the walling in the roof obscured the workings above it.

We did not understand what we had seen at the time, and were staggered at what we considered to be a desecration of the mine, and put it down to the work of 'cowboys' rather than the old miners. Fuller understanding was to come later.

At the junction of Old Rake Vein and Miller Cross Cut, there was what years ago I imagined to be a stope. By 1979 I had changed my mind and reasoned that it was a shaft leading on to an upper level. My brother and I even thought there would be some connection between this shaft and the hopper at the beginning of Miller Cross Cut. In 1980 to my great surprise, my brother expressed his determination to climb into this shaft as we saw it and carried through what must surely have been a bold piece of climbing for a novice. Fortunately he possesses great stores of patience, is meticulous and thorough. The rock was very poor in places, but our equipment was equal to the task.

Unhappily our iron stakes ran out just as we were about to enter what proved to be a large stope. So we were not dealing with a shaft after all, but rather a rise into ore bearing ground. With some difficulty, I managed to climb the rise and could gauge that we were at the foot of a huge working which still contained a large vein of fluorspar. Above my head the rise seemed to go on up, a circumstance that puzzled us at the time. Away to the left, I could see what appeared to be galvanised air pipes in position, probably intended to blow air into the upper part of the workings above. I remember, as I stood precariously perched on one of the irons, feeling that I was out of my league. My brother wanted to complete the climb the following day, but I dissuaded him and have in retrospect regretted that we did not enter the workings. However, there was another matter weighing heavily upon my mind at the time.

In the wall of the level in Old Rake Vein just a stones throw away there was a large hole. I had known of it for many years, and at first thought of it as a working beneath the floor and imagined it to be some 30 feet deep. However, by the simple expedient of casting a stone into it, we discovered that we were standing at the head of a very deep hole. We plumbed it with heavy irons attached to a 100 foot rope and to our satisfaction felt it hit the bottom. I had constructed a rope ladder about 88 feet long from polypropylene ropes, each having a breaking strain of one and a half tons. Being seven years my junior my brother volunteered to make the descent. He was going to need all the strength that those seven years less would give. The most fearful aspect of this affair was that we were facing an entirely unknown situation, both as respects our ability to handle a rope ladder, which is entirely different from its rigid cousin, and with regard to its suitability and design.

We realised that we were dealing with a rise that sank down on to the George Level 100 feet below, and the prospect of gaining admittance to this elusive mine filled us with eager anticipation. At this time, we were uncertain of the exact depth of this hole. Tension was high as I secured the 100 foot safety rope to my brother and began to feed it round an iron rail, as the descent slowly began. Because of an error in our method, this support was only effective for 50 feet, and beyond it he found himself dangling and on his own.

The rise was not straight and at one stage the ladder was touching one if its walls and several feet later the one opposite. This required the climber to change from one side of the ladder to the other, an unpleasant task whilst hanging in the gloom an unknown distance from the floor. Eighty feet down, he bottomed on to rocks that choked the rise. Dripping water percolated between them to the level beneath his feet. We were bitterly disappointed by this turn of events, and wondered how such a thing could be. The rise was sound in all respects and a few stemples remained fixed from wall to wall. How was it that it could be blocked in this way, we wondered? Although we did not

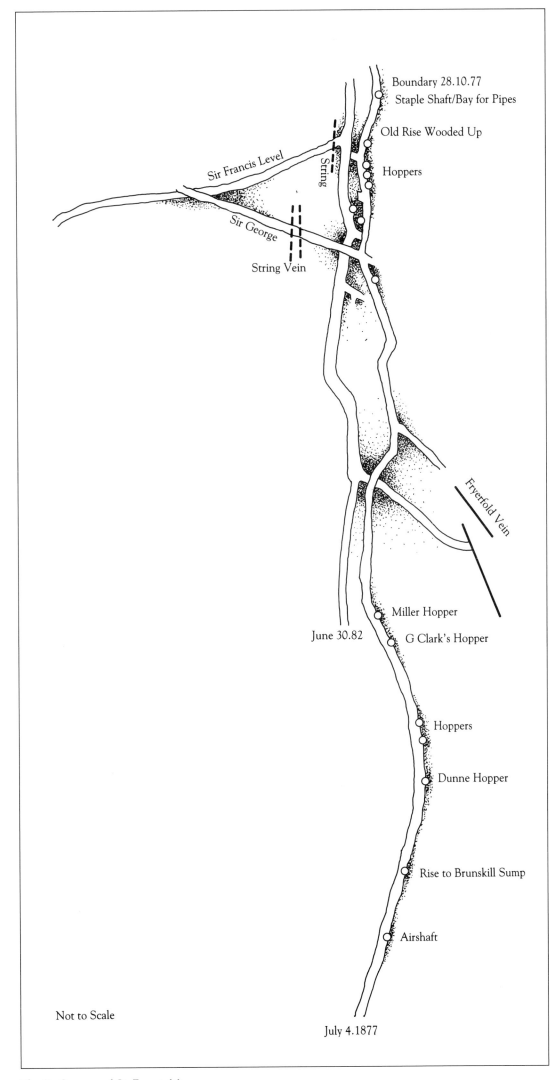

Boundary 28.10.77
Staple Shaft/Bay for Pipes

Old Rise Wooded Up

Sir Francis Level

String

Hoppers

Sir George

String Vein

Fryerfold Vein

Weak wall supported by rock drills, Fryerfold Vein.

Miller Hopper

June 30.82

G Clark's Hopper

Hoppers

Dunne Hopper

Rise to Brunskill Sump

Airshaft

Not to Scale

July 4.1877

The Sir George and Sir Francis Mines

fully understand these new facts that were confronting us, they seemed yet a further desecration of the mine, and we could not but connect them with what we had seen in Old Rake Vein.

It was now time for the strength-sapping ascent. An extremely difficult task had become almost impossible because the ladder had been constructed with the rungs too far apart. Communications between us were poor because of the conditions which separated us. I watched the tension on the ladder anxiously, and as my brother came nearer I could hear his heavy breathing. His survival instinct had brought him up some 50 feet, but he was completely exhausted. I then thought to lower him a rope but mistakenly threw it down, creating a dangerous situation, for 30 feet down it would pack a dangerous clout. Providence, however, favoured us, and with my help the hazardous climb was soon at an end as Bunting Level and comparative safety was reached.

Our great hope of entering the elusive George Level had been dashed. For us, it was 'the one that got away'. There were so many features of interest that we should have loved to examine, since clearly it was a level that must have been driven after Bunting but before Sir Francis. By June 1877 it had been driven 530 fathoms east from the level head as it joined Old Rake Vein. The miners during their prospecting uncovered Old Man's workings in the shape of a hand cut level and an old rise still fully wooded up.

Near to the rise that we tested which dropped on to Old Rake Vein was the Fryerfold Level. Some 50 feet into it was a sump that was down 6 fathoms and contained good ore. A letter, probably from Simon Cherry to Sir Francis Denys Bart in July 1884, informed him that the sump had been abandoned because of water problems. West of the Sir George Cross Cut to the vein there were no less than five hoppers over a distance of 40 fathoms. Further west still is Staple Shaft, which surfaces to the west of Bunting Beck, just above Priscilla Level, and carries the massive engine supply pipe via the Sir George on down to the Sir Francis Engine House. At the foot of this shaft in Sir George was a bay where pipes were stored during the construction of the engine. Yet further west, the level was used to put in rises to both the Priscilla above and Sir Francis beneath.

We tested the engine shaft from the surface and found it blocked with 'deads' 40 feet down. It was our last attempt to enter the Sir George, which stubbornly resisted all our endeavours at penetration. A previous effort had been made to enter the level from Priscilla with similar results. The George Level mouth is now buried under rubble but it was impassable in the early 1960's.

We began to take an interest in the shaft that brought the pipe into the Sir Francis engine house. It had received the same kind of treatment as many another. Deads had been thrown down it and they blocked the level just beyond the engine house. It finally dawned upon us that it rose to the Sir George which was 200 feet above and there was a good chance that it was still open.

I made an abortive journey to the engine shaft near Priscilla to measure the size of the pipe sections. Snow had fallen a few days earlier and the journey proved hazardous. The surrounding hills clothed in their cloak of white were breathtakingly beautiful, and as I picked my way forward the silence was deafening. I fell to reflecting upon the harsh life of the miner whose life expectancy was no more than 47 years. The well-known complaints from which they suffered such as lung disease and rheumatics were augmented by the general health scourges of the time. I was reminded of this as I examined the tombstone of James Jackson and family. He lost a two-year-old daughter in 1859, but eight years later he experienced the most savage blow with the loss of Mary, his 33-year-old wife. The following year his sons, Richard, seven and James, five, died within a month of each other, cut down with mumps and scarlet fever.

Bunting Level

This tumbling stream near the village of Marrick in Swaledale is pictured by Nigel Whitfield/DST

02/01/01

[...] bombs sen[...] in [...] North

warning. A spokesman said: [...]yone connected with agricul[...]e or animals, either directly or [...]irectly should treat their mail [...]h caution. Any unsolicited [...]kages, which for any reason [...]use suspicion – particurlarly [...]ns not bearing any indication [...]o their source – should be left [...]ouched and local police be [...]rted."

[...]he warning was extended to [...]ople sending packages who [...]e been asked to clearly label [...] packaging in order to readily [...]ntify the sender.

[...]o far injuries have been mini[...]l with three people being [...]ghtly injured.

[...] woman at an estate agents in Patrington, East Yorkshire, suffered serious eye injuries after opening a letter containing a device. The firm was said to deal with livestock auctions

In the Ripon attack, in January, a farmer suffered facial injuries after he opened a package containing nails. A week earlier, a letter bomb was sent to the owner of a pest control business, in Congleton, Cheshire. It was opened by the owner's six-year-old daughter, who suffered leg wounds.

This week only one of the bombs, in Penrith, exploded. Army experts made the other two bombs safe. No-one was hurt.

So far no group has yet claimed responsibility but police are convinced animal rights extremists are behind the attacks.

Seven police forces are involved in an investigation overseen by detectives from North Yorkshire. The force's deputy chief constable Peter Walker said this week: "Yet again, we have indiscriminate attacks on law-abiding people.

"How volunteers working for a charity can be viewed as a legitimate target in a bombing campaign is beyond me."

As well as attacks in Ripon and Masham, bombs have been sent to addresses in Cheshire, Humberside, North Wales, the West Midlands and Northumbria.

[...]ts customers have been offered alternatives

company defends stop pager service

BY FAY NAYMAN

[...]eper system which is often [...]d to wake medical personnel [...]d can be heard and used any[...]ere in the country regardless of [...]nal strength or coverage.

[...]e told the *D&S Times*: [...]utchison Telecom and Orange [...]ve given us excellent service for [...] past three years for all our [...]ergency call outs.

["]Our pager number is used by [...]east 24 hospital wards and de[...]rtments and 47 insurance [...]mpanies for emergency med[...]l repatriation.

["]We now have to find another [...]ovider, change our number and [...]pe that everyone we inform re[...]embers to change their [...]ords."

[...]Mr Merry was told by Hutchi[...]n Telecom that the service was [...] longer financially viable and [...]t a buyer for the service had [...]t been found.

"They make millions of pounds in profit," he said. "Why cut such an important service that is used in many cases to save lives."

An Orange spokesman confirmed that pagers did operate regardless of signal strength or coverage, but denied that the company was putting profits before people.

He said: "We are not putting profits before lives. Customers are choosing to buy mobile phones instead of pagers.

"We accept there will be certain professions where this won't be suitable but every effort is being made to contact all customers to work out the best options for them."

Options include:

● Orange Assistance – an operator answers using your name and texts you the message. One-off connection charge of £10 excluding VAT and a monthly subscription of £20 excluding VAT.

● Orange Messenger – Calls answered by operator using a standard greeting, text message sent to you. No set-up costs, 25p per message excluding VAT.

● Arrangements to transfer paging service to another operator.

Mr Merry added: "At the moment we have the service we need for only £7 a month.

"With a pager you are never out of touch, that is not the same with a mobile phone text service which only works depending on operator coverage and signal strength."

Hutchison Telecom has offered a free Orange phone and free connection to Orange Talk 60 or a free pay as you go Orange phone with £50 of free talk time, to all pager customers.

Alternatively customers can choose from a selection of promotional gifts to the value of £50.

[...]e head hails year of
[...]h and achievement

Squires, Harriet Taylor award for NNEB student of the year; Cherylnne Weston, Glaxo Wellcome prize BTEC National

The long distances walked by the miner to his place of work has not gone unnoticed. In order to use their time profitably they would knit, and should they meet with another as they journeyed, they would have 'six stitches', their expression for a gossip.

When finally I reached the shaft it was packed solid with snow, which frustrated my purpose. My general irritation was assuaged by the sheer beauty of the morning as I contemplated the clattering waters leaping between the boulders at Botcher Gill. The massive one foot wide pipe proved to have sections nine feet long.

The logistical problems associated with attempting to climb it convinced me that it was beyond us. So Sir George would not yield us its secrets and we had to be content in the knowledge that on two occasions we were within a few feet of it.

Sir Francis Inlet Pipe supplying water to the Sir Francis Engines.

Old Surrender Smelt Mill.

5

The Great Escape at Eldorado

No other discovery that we ever made caused us greater excitement and trauma than Eldorado. It was a good example of a rise to ore bearing ground that we ran across, incorporating a hopper down which 'deads' and more particularly successfully won ore had been dropped. A steady stream of water poured from it in 1978, and my first attempt at a photograph, though not unsuccessful, did destroy my camera as an effective instrument.

In 1979, there was the great drought and during that year water ceased to tumble from the rise. We decided to explore it, and with only hand torches to aid us the task was begun. We were not unaware of the hazards associated with such an assignment, because of the age and state of the timbers. My brother led the way, cautiously inching his way up the rise. At about 40 feet, he reported that he was entering a small drift to the right. He expressed great disappointment upon discovering that it quickly came to an end. On my insistance that the rise would have more to show for itself, he was encouraged to probe further and noticed some wooden boards above his head. The beam of his torch shone through some cracks, revealing empty space behind. I was greatly encouraged when this fact was reported and was eager with anticipation for what should be discovered.

Our equipment was taken up on a rope and I then followed. One or two timbers were decidedly loose, but I was able to reach the drift very quickly by using the old method adopted by the miners, which was by straddling the rise and stepping on the timbers conveniently placed on either side of it, although one or two were missing from one side at the bottom.

My brother climbed from the drift for a further ten feet and began to move the boards that were blocking his way. He clambered into a sizeable working and triumphantly announced that he had found a miner's pickaxe. We had always nurtured the hope that we might enter an upper main level of the mine by means of this rise, so it was with some disappointment that he intimated that we had not succeeded in this objective. His disappointment, however, was soon tempered by his excitement at having discovered a perfectly preserved wooden tub perched on a small gauge railway. Now it was my turn to ascend to the workings. All went well at first, and in the general gloom, I was able to make out a sizeable working above my head, which clearly in the past had been mined clean of lead ore. The hand torch that I was using at the time was old and had lost the bulk of its silver reflecting surface, a point worth mentioning since it helps to explain what followed.

In order to leave the rise, I eased myself forward putting my full weight on my arms. In the gloom, I had not appreciated that what I had taken to be the rock side of the rise top was, in fact, an old wooden board covered with debris. It had not been particularly well placed and instantly gave way under my weight. In the twinkling of an eye, I was plunging down the 50 foot rise to the horse level below. A horrified Peter, seeing me disappear out of sight, gritted his teeth and braced himself to break my fall, since we were roped together. The likelihood is, of course, that far from his preventing my fall, he more likely than not would have joined me. In the following agonising moments that seemed like an eternity, all that my brother could hear was the roar of falling material which in such a confined space is frighteningly loud, a noise that he took to be me falling down the rise. He was sick at heart at what was nothing short of an unmitigated disaster, but he had heard no cry from me at any time, and as the noise from the falling debris subsided he was mystified that his rope had never tightened. Finally, after what seemed an age, Peter found his voice and the courage to try to communicate with me.

"John, are you there," he called.

To his utter amazement and relief I responded.

For my part, events had moved so quickly that I had no time to feel anything. I uttered no word. Far from falling to the bottom of the rise on my downward descent, I had dropped ten feet and my foot had miraculously caught the firm rock edge of the small drift below. This had the effect of pushing me backward to smash up against the wooden hopper. I was now precariously perched 40 feet above the level laid at an angle across the rise with nothing more serious than a severely bleeding finger to show for my experience. I had had a most miraculous escape from almost certain death and saw the protecting hand of providence in these matters, which increased my conviction that it was my duty to the old miners to continue with my research.

The Old Miners Tub.

Hopper, Old Rake Vein.

Shakily I climbed to the top of the rise again, and gingerly found my way to safety. Deeply relieved at such a great escape, Peter bitterly assailed me for my carelessness. I made no response, probably being too shocked to do so, and strangely I never allowed these events to seriously affect me, although I was much more careful when climbing was involved again.

We put these matters behind us, and beginning to examine the tub, we found it to be in perfect repair. In order to prevent it falling down the rise the miners had put a rock drill through the spokes of the front wheels. From the time that I had taken up this work, I had always secretly cherished the hope that one day I might stumble across some old miners' tools. Such an event, of course, would be most unlikely, but here the impossible had happened.

We began to examine a small durk drift going in broadly the opposite direction to the one ten feet below. It struck off at the top of the rise and at the base of a huge stope that had been worked out. I stumbled upon a hammer and rock drill, whilst my brother found five pickaxes neatly stacked one on top of the other. We began to feel that we were on hallowed ground. Our discoveries were not complete for we happened on a shovel, a turnkey and yet another rock drill. Peter found a winch surrounded by one inch hemp rope that was so rotten that it fell apart in his hand, we then stumbled upon an old pop bottle advertising the firm Russell and Croft of Richmond. Mr. Harold Brown remembered that this concern had ceased trading before the First World War. Finally we came upon an old newspaper, the Stockton and Darlington Times and Richmond and Ripon Chronicle. Inevitably we saw the possibility of dating the work of the miners concerned. I remember seeing reference to the Titanic which sank in April 1912, but the date on the paper seemed to elude us, and we all but gave up. When hope was all but gone, there it was, March 23rd, 1912, a few months after the collapse of mining in Arkengarthdale when there were still men who believed that a lucky strike could transform their fortunes.

What I think had happened was that a small partnership of six men had refurbished an old rise/hopper and put in the drift to a vein nearby. Miners of a much earlier generation had worked out the huge stope above our heads over 100 years earlier, and it had been rich in lead. Their successors at the turn of the 20th century were hoping to exploit an area that had been left unexplored by previous generations. Mining in Swaledale was on its last legs in 1912 and all operations of any consequence had ceased. The intriguing question is, why did the miners leave so much of their equipment behind? It is a question to which there can be no certain answer, but their surprising behaviour was to provide us with an enormous success. Little wonder that we christened the rise 'Eldorado', a suitably descriptive name since the one given to it originally had long been forgotten. Examining the facts available along with the known situation at the time, there is more than a hint of pathos in our discovery. Could it be that the miners had concluded that the end had come and there was no point in carrying on? Had they left the tools behind in the forlorn hope that a more favourable time might arise? Alas, it was not to be.

It was falling dusk when we came from the mine to be greeted by kindly friends out looking for us. We had experienced a great triumph, but the fearful events that took place at Eldorado which could so easily have made our triumph a tragedy, we kept much to ourselves.

As we passed near to the ruins of the Old Surrender Smelt Mill on the Kearton Road bound for home, we could just make out Cringley Hall huddled amongst its surrounding trees. William Gill of Low Row, born in the mid 19th century, identified this now deserted and crumbling property as Gang Hall, which was so intimately associated with the history of lead mining in Swaledale from the 1690's on. It was used by Philip Swale and partner when undertaking developments at Old Gang and Lownathwaite giving shelter and warmth to many a miner.

Several years were to elapse before we returned to Eldorado and by this time we possessed better equipment and were more able to understand what had been taking place there. We were quite convinced that we should stumble upon a main upper level but our aspirations in this respect were not realised. We must have climbed 90 to 100 feet above the horse level and still the worked out vein was going on up. We trampled on a carpet of large fluorspar boulders that had been rejected. All that part of the vein that had been impregnated with lead had been removed but literally tons of fluorspar remained at our feet.

Our old maps indicated that we should be near such a level and yet for all our searchings we could find nothing of it. Since the miners would follow the vein the level had to be nearby. The vein would almost certainly have been worked from the upper level but now that communication had been made with the more important lower level which had transport and location advantages, the one above I suspect had been arched over to protect it from falling debris and probably the unwanted rock upon which I was standing concealed any sign of it.

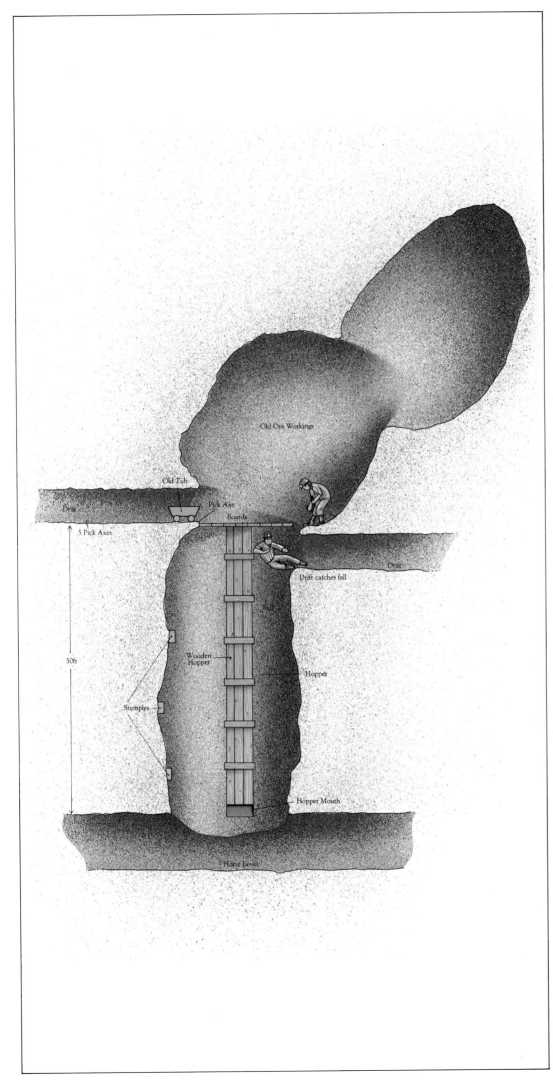

Old Ore Workings

Old Tub

Pick Axe

Drift

Boards

5 Pick Axes

Drift catches fall

Drift

Fall

50ft

Wooden Hopper

Hopper

Stemples

Hopper Mouth

Horse Level

Old winch abandoned in back filled drift.

Looking from the top of the rise/hopper, Eldorado.

Eldorado.

Level House looking on to Dolphins Whim.

6

The Brandy Bottle

I first entered the Brandy Bottle Incline in 1965. There are two inclines and it is said they were driven side by side to meet the Fryerfold Vein in about 1815 as part of Frederick Hall's grand design for the Old Gang Mines. His intention was to station a steam engine on the surface there and the fact that there are two inclines suggests he may have contemplated installing a reciprocating haulage system using the inclined plane, such ideas being very fashionable at that time. The principle of such a system would be that whilst one set of tubs were on the surface, the other would be at the loading point undergound.

Brandy Bottle Incline. The parallel incline is just visible to the right.

From the descriptions that we have been given, it does appear that during the late eighteenth and early nineteenth centuries the Old Gang Mines had not kept abreast of the latest technical achievements. Hall set out to build upon the developments commissioned by Lord Pomfret and represented a much needed breath of fresh air for the management of the mines.

His plans were far seeing and would 'pay off' in the long term. Unhappily neither he nor his employers, the Aldersons, were to reap the rich rewards of his work. That pleasure was to be the lot of Jaques and Company, who took over the lease of the mines in 1828 and within a few years their output was consistently in excesss of 1,200 tons of lead per year over a ten year period. Some of Hall's ideas were never put into practice and the right hand incline was allowed to fall into decay whilst the other was at first inauspiciously used as an entry and exit for horses, being used in connection with underground haulage. Some years later a whim gin (winding engine) was erected at the head of the incline and it was then used to haul ore to the surface, thus redeeming in some measure the investment of former years. It is possible to wade for a few yards in the Fryerfold Vein at the foot of the incline, but strangely there is no sign of the second incline to be seen there, suggesting that it was never completed.

On my first visit to the Incline and about half way down it, I came upon what appeared to be part of an old Anderson air raid shelter, and in those days sitting on the rails close to it was one of the old large iron tubs. I was fearfully looking down a large deep gash in the floor, which I recognised as some form of working. It was not possible from that vantage point to gauge the extent of it, and near at hand it was possible to follow the same gash going on up above me in the hillside. As has already been noted a level went off from the incline here, one limb of it turning east to cut the Brandy Bottle Vein before it travels on into Surrender ground, which was connected by a rise to the C.B. Mines and Moulds Level. The other continues on to the Fryerfold Vein making a junction with it near to the Bell Shaft. I passed on down the incline that day to the Fryerfold Vein, and across the years what little thought I gave to the Brandy Bottle Vein merely served to confuse me. It seemed so different to the other workings that I had visited. How, in fact, was it worked, and where was the level that gave access?

By 1980 my brother, who had been studying our maps in relation to visits to the Black Cross Cut, was suggesting that the shaft responsible for blocking the cross cut below had been driven between it and the Brandy Bottle Vein. This seemed a reasonable suggestion, but the only way that it could be confirmed was for a descent of the frightening hole previously mentioned. The matter might have remained just an academic discussion had I not made a rare week end visit to the mines in 1980 with two friends. Several days prior to the projected visit, the rain literally poured from the heavens. That weekend was most instructive. I had never seen so much water awash in the mines before, and was reminded of the appalling conditions accepted by the old miners as a matter of course. The project that I had in mind was aborted because the height of the water in the level I had a mind to enter was much too great, and there was the possibility that temporarily we could have been cut off underground. Looking for substitutes, the Brandy Bottle came to mind, and so it was that I found myself descending a rope ladder for the first time, supported by my colleagues above. It was not usual for water to be much in evidence here, but today was different, as it descended in a steady stream upon my head.

I seemed to be descending into a vein which was about two to three feet wide. There was a considerable amount of guange material left in it which was clearly visible. I finally landed on a heap of small muddy black shale, and was able to make considerable progress along the vein.

Finally it dropped several feet and could be seen travelling on, but I was unable to go any further. Where was the rise from the Black Cross Cut, I wondered? Perhaps it was further on from where I had been. Where was all the water going that was dropping into the vein? There was no evidence of a build up at all. I came away convinced that there was a rise there, but had not found any evidence of it. It must therefore be buried under the rubble, I reasoned.

I doubt whether I would have returned to that place, had it not been for my brother's strong urgings. Two years had elapsed since I was last there and the incline had clearly deteriorated. With the aid of a block and tackle arrangement we were both able to descend into the vein. We had quickly discovered that swinging precariously on a rope ladder bore no resemblance whatsoever to the more stable ladder used by the painter and decorator. I was the first down and whilst receiving a heavy bag of irons from above, they broke loose from the rope and thudded into the mud after falling some 30 feet. Happily I had taken up a safe position, but somewhat philosophically I acknowledged to myself that such incidents seemed to go hand in hand with this job.

The visit to Brandy Bottle Vein on this occasion proved most productive. Amid the surrounding gloom, aided by the piercing light on my helmet, I carefully looked for the hidden rise. There it was, almost obscured by the debris that filled and overlaid it. My brother noticed a three inch pipe running into it. It was engulfed by the debris that choked the rise. What could it have been? Had it anything to do with the engine located by Hall on the Fryerfold Vein? Inspecting the vein, we could recognise large quantities of fluorspar and calcite interdispersed with small nuggets of lead.

We progressed along the vein to the place where it dropped some twelve to 15 feet. It was a part of our plan to cut our ladder and climb down to investigate the area so far unvisited. I had unearthed a small section of iron rail and we jammed it between the two walls, secured the ladder and climbed down. It was now clear that we were travelling along the vein, the floor of which had once contained a narrow gauge railway. The rubble down which we descended had been dumped down into the vein from the Middle Level. The vein that had been left in was impregnated with lead and clearly visible above our heads. We were in fact somewhat astonished at the quantity of it that seemed in evidence. After a considerable distance our way was blocked by a run in.

Pillar of rock left in to support the roof, Flinchert Level.

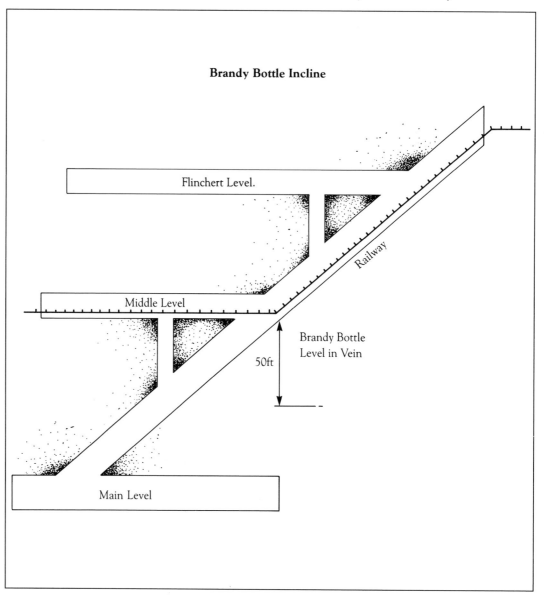

Brandy Bottle Incline

Flinchert Level.

Railway

Middle Level

Brandy Bottle
Level in Vein

50ft

Main Level

Slowly we returned to our exit point and the hazardous business of getting out of the hole began. Without our block and tackle arrangement neither of us would have succeeded, but because of one or two simple mischances, for me it proved a half hour nightmare and to crown it all, I left a large section of our ladder down in the vein and we had to retrieve it about two months later. It was now clear that the rise from the Black Cross Cut came into the Brandy Bottle Vein, as the spoil running into its head was the same as that spewing from its foot. At the junction of the incline with the vein a section of broad gauge railway branched away from the main line stopping at the vein edge, suggesting that ore was taken out of it and hauled to the surface up the incline. Near here a shaft had been sunk down on to the lower half of the incline. Rails were never put into this lower section although it was probably Hall's intention to use the whole of the incline, and ore could have been lowered from the Middle Level down this shaft to waiting tubs below.

It is often a matter of amazement that interesting and important features within a mine can be readily accessible but so easily missed. As we made our way up the incline on the way out to the surface that day, we looked at a shaft that had been driven just above the rails. It was some 30 feet high and we could see a drift in one side of it. We speculated on its significance but could reach no convincing conclusion. Some 25 yards further up the incline and about 50 yards from the mine entrance, there is a section that had been shored up in the distant past. Close by is a feature that has always excited interest, a pillar of rock left in by the miners to support the roof. Previously I had carried out a cursory investigation of this working as I had imagined it, but on this occasion our probings were much more thorough. We found ourselves moving along a level of whose existence we had been totally unaware. We came upon, and looked down, the shaft over the rails which had caused so much speculation. It was now perfectly clear that we were in the Flint Chert Level in Brandy Bottle Vein and the shaft was intended by Hall for the lowering of ore down to tubs waiting on the incline. I now realised that earlier we had been privileged to descend into the Main 12 fathom Limestone in the Brandy Bottle Vein, which in the hey day of its working must have cut a magnificent sight. Hall's intention for the incline then appears to have been to collect ore from the three major levels in the mine, but the cost of the project combined with a lack of sympathy for such bold thinking was probably the root cause of his exit from the company after only four years.

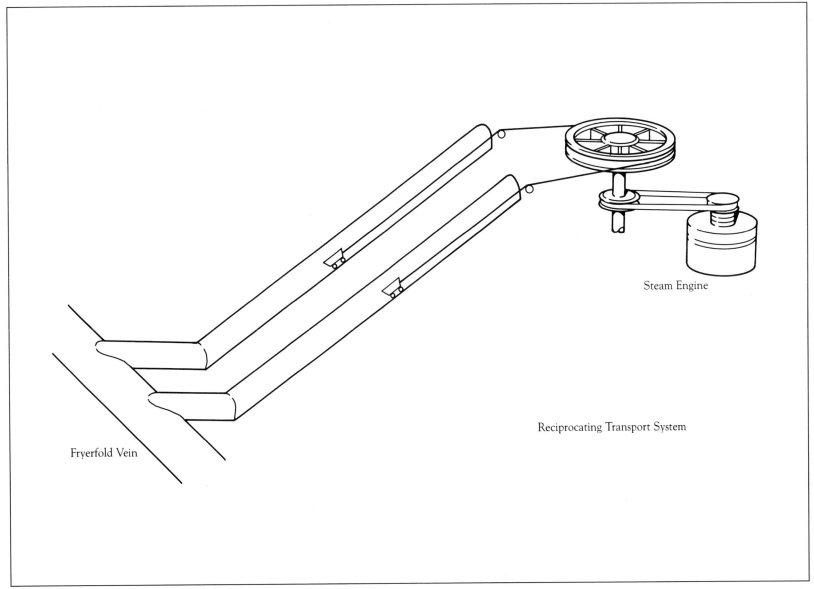

Steam Engine

Reciprocating Transport System

Fryerfold Vein

As previously suggested, I had always felt that there was something strangely different about the Brandy Bottle workings and an examination of all the circumstances suggests a certain unusualness in the way they were exploited in the Main Lime at least. Veins are usually approached by levels beneath them, and from rises they are worked upward and along. In the case of the Brandy Bottle with access afforded by the incline, it was necessary at least initially to work the vein downward and along, in other words like a sump, hence the need for drainage to the Black Cross Cut.

In 1870 Ralph Place was pencilling in some recommended trials on to a map. One of his suggestions envisaged was a cross cut from Deans to the Brandy Bottle Vein. Deans Vein was worked in the Main Lime from a durk drift until 1887, when the Old Gang Company surrendered its lease. I've often wondered about that cross cut, but now have little doubt that had we been able to travel far enough along Brandy Bottle Vein, we would have found it and gained access to Deans Vein which cuts the Fryerfold Vein.

There was a surprising absence of water in the vein. Indeed, had there been a running stream our explorations would have been drastically curtailed. Perhaps it is escaping somewhere else along the network. If efforts were made to enter the Underset Limestone in the Deans and Brandy Bottle Veins, sumps would have been used, and we saw no physical evidence of such activity in the eastern end of the workings.

One of our great disappointments had always been that we had failed to pass from one major level to another. Putting all the evidence together however, it is clear that the Incline gives access to the Flint Chert, Middle and Main Levels, which is perhaps only to be expected. The incline is rather like a deep shaft laid over at an angle. The location of the Flintchert Level has already been mentioned. At the top of the Brandy Bottle Level in the Vein is the Middle Level, which takes off from this place and serves to give access to the Black (shale) and Red (sandstone) Beds. Finally, at the foot of the Incline is the Main Level on the Fryerfold Vein, giving access to the Main Limestone.

Despite now having a clearer understanding concerning the Brandy Bottle Mine, we are still left musing on the event or incident that led to its acquiring such an intriguing name. The structure of the mine that I saw showed no resemblance to a bottle and as a mere speculation I suspect that one or more of the miners took their drink to work in a brandy bottle. The appearance of such a bottle would lead to ribald comments amongst the miners since their lot would be more to contemplate brandy than to consume it. Bottles sometimes get left behind and the vein would come to be associated with them. The vein where the brandy bottles are found, could soon become the Brandy Bottle Vein.

However, it must be conceded that such information has slipped behind the curtain of time. But what is in a name? it may be asked. That such information could be both interesting and illuminating derives from our knowledge of how the Water Blast Vein acquired its name. Our tidings come to us third hand, but initially was passed on by Bolt Tom Coates. It was the case in the old days for all of the miners to be known by nicknames, Cony Tom, Katy Willie, Curly Tom, Smash Willie; the list is endless.

Bolt Tom said that in the eighteenth century the miners were driving on to a vein, when they blasted into an underground lake. Twenty-four miners perished that day, they never had a chance, and the two pit ponies were washed out of the level. Eighteen of these men came from the small hamlet of Booze. The anguish and misery suffered as a result of this disaster can hardly be imagined now, as it left behind it a trail of widows and fatherless children. In a small community of this size, scarcely a household could have escaped the cruel clutches of the angel of death. What is in a name indeed!

There was a strange sequel to these tragic events many years later. A gang of miners were making their way up the same level, when they heard the unmistakable rumbling of approaching tubs. Being totally familiar with this type of situation, they jumped to the side of the rails to allow them through. To their amazement, however, no tubs appeared. Astonished and fearful, they could not but connect these strange happenings with the terrible loss of life that had occurred long years before.

Looking up Brandy Bottle Incline from Flinchert Level.

Inside Brandy Bottle Vein.

Waiting to exit from Brandy Bottle Vein.

43

View from Bunting across to Lownathwaite Mines.

7

The Search for the Black Cross Cut

I vividly recall in the early 1960's sitting in the congregation of Reeth Methodist Chapel with my mind wandering and, alas, not concentrating upon the sermon. I was fingering a small map of the Old Gang Mines. The map told me that the Black Cross Cut was near the foot of the Brandy Bottle Incline and I was intent upon finding it. This incline drops 100 fathoms on to the Fryerfold Vein. I visited it with a friend, and at its foot we came to a sort of sump containing about two feet of water covering some old tubs. A few feet from the bottom of the incline is the Fryerfold Vein. It is only possible to see it for a few yards, as it has been subject to run-ins, but it is readily visible to the experienced observer. I did not, however, possess enough experience and this led to my making a fundamental misjudgement. To the left of the bottom of the incline is a small passage almost filled with water. I took this to be the Fryerfold Vein and it seemed that I must enter it if I was to find the Black Cross Cut.

Getting into the passage way presented a frightening prospect, especially as it contained so much water. To ensure a measure of safety, I hit upon the idea of putting a car inner tube around my middle. Equipped simply with helmet and hand torch, I sank for the first time into the cold water of this level buoyed up by the inner tube. I can remember very little of the journey today, save that I was terrified with every step forward. I kept scuffing my foot along the wall, hoping to discover a concealed entrance, for I had heard that to enter the Black Cross Cut it was necessary to go up a shaft. Finally, I came to a blockage, but there did not seem enough room for me to get through. At the time I thought an ore working was in front of me, and as it was impossible to go any further, I thankfully retreated.

Some years later, in 1979, I met a man sitting at the entrance to the Brandy Bottle Incline. He told me that some years earlier he had gone through the Black Cross Cut and come out at the mouth of the Hard Level. He described the first watery stretch, which I knew only too well, passing through the old doorway, and shortly after coming up into the dry. Unfortunately his further information served to confuse me, particularly as he mentioned the importance of getting into the Sun Vein. The Sun Vein was located in a different part of the mine, and I think he must have been referring to the North Rake.

Perhaps that chance meeting turned my thoughts to the Black Cross cut again, and later that year my brother and I arrived at the foot of the Brandy Bottle incline. Through the years, I had often wondered what was on the other side of the blockage, and now within a short time, I was determined to find out. My brother had no enthusiasm for the task that I had in mind, and I found it difficult to enlist his support. To encourage him, I carried out a reconnaissance, and later took up our photographic equipment with our simple transport system, washing up bowls inside car inner tubes. I had forgotten how dreadful the journey was. The level was only five feet high, and my helmet continually scraped along the roof, forcing my face into the water. It seemed that I would never reach my destination. I saw the old doorway, and soon after the blockage that I had remembered from years before. It seemed to me then the worst 130 yards that I had ever travelled. Finally, we came up together and squeezed through the hole finding the roof immediately higher. To our left a shaft had spewed out a mass of mud and rubbish, which had all but blocked the level. To our right, what I had thought to be a stope appeared to be a shallow chamber. I was firmly of the opinion then that we were in the Fryerfold Vein and that the Black Cross Cut was at the top of the shaft to my left, and hence inaccessible.

The level was in the most appalling condition. Great lumps of shale had fallen from the roof, and it was very difficult to move along at any speed. We came upon a hopper and reasoned that we had reached Deans Vein. The hopper seemed to go up 30 feet, although it was difficult to see with our poor torches. Some 15 yards later we came to yet another shaft, and after some 720 yards there was a hole at the side of the floor. Water was pouring through it into workings below. A run-in barred our path and we thought we had been on the other side of it at Rigg Vein in Bunting Level. I was very surprised at the lack of mining activity in a vein so celebrated as the Fryerfold, and contemplating our surroundings we shivered miserably. We returned to the surface puzzled men and had many long discussions about what we had seen and where we had been. During the ensuing year, my brother suggested that we had in fact been in the Black Cross Cut all along, and he reminded me that the level had been in black shale. We determined to settle the matter beyond doubt, and on our next trip we took a compass. It was a very wet year, and the first 130 yards seemed worse than ever. Standing in the chest high water, I took a compass reading which confirmed that we were indeed heading south. So my brother was right, and we had been in the Black Cross Cut all the time. Now the various features that we had seen would have to be considered again, in the light of our new discovery.

We are informed that in driving the Black Cross Cut above the Hard Level network in about 1814/15, Frederick Hall found it necessary to put a steam engine into Fryerfold Vein to pump the water into the cross cut. No record of the engine appeared in the mine inventory of 1824, suggesting that it had been removed. I began to suspect that the small chamber in the right hand wall was the former site of the steam engine, particularly as it was situated only a few yards from a shaft.

The installation of the steam engine should be seen in the context of Hall's complete plan for that part of the mine. Our information is that he drove the Brandy Bottle Incline down on to Fryerfold Vein, intending to use it in conjunction with a steam engine to haul ore to the surface. In 1818 he left the Old Gang Company, being in dispute with his employers, and his ideas in respect of the Incline were never put into practice. Instead, we understand ore was lifted by whim gin 32 fathoms up Bell Shaft from Middle Level, and 47 fathoms up Willans Shaft from Main Level to the surface for transport to the smelt mill at Hard Level mouth.

A main sump is recorded as being located on Fryerfold Vein beneath Bell Shaft. It is not therefore surprising to find the Black Cross Cut cutting the vein beneath it.

As we pushed on down the level, we made what to us was a sensational discovery. Close to the small chamber previously mentioned, and almost totally obscured by massive lumps of shale that had fallen out of the roof, we found two large iron tubs still chained together. They were so well concealed that we had passed over them on our previous visit without being aware of them. Could this cross cut have been a waygate for the transport of ore, I wondered? But Raistrick and Jennings, in their book *Lead Mining in the Pennines*, affirm that it was to be used only as a drain. Some 150 yards further on down the cross cut, we came to the old hopper. Our previous belief that it went on to Deans Vein was correct enough, for that vein runs over the cross cut. Similarly, the shaft 15 yards further on was another rise on to Deans Vein. As we moved along, travelling began to improve, and we could stand up with ease. We could now clearly see a broad gauge railway for most of the way down the cross cut as far as we could travel. The two tubs further up were no fluke.

We made a simple ladder, and climbed down the hole at the side of the cross cut. I reasoned that we were close to the North Rake Vein. There was only a drop of 12 feet and I walked down a short sloping passage carpeted with fallen rocks. Soon I was confronted with what seemed like an underground lake, with the top of a level just visible. My immediate thought was that I would never get through such an obstruction to the Old Rake, for I baulked at the prospect of trying to reach it. On the way back to the ladder, I noticed a small hole with water filtering away. I scrambled through, and realised that I was in North Vein Cross Cut. It was about 220 yards long, and contained rails all the way down to the Old Rake Vein.

Having followed me down, my brother found that I had disappeared. He thought that I had gone into the water and, like me, hesitated. He could hear a strange rhythmic thumping noise, which was in fact me exploring in North Rake Vein Cross Cut, and it caused him some concern at the time. He was startled by a flashing light, and heard my apparently disembodied voice. I beckoned him to follow and, squeezing through, he joined me in the cross cut.

We were particularly intrigued by a large shaft in the cross cut. We wondered what its function

Remains of old tubs at foot of Brandy Bottle Incline.

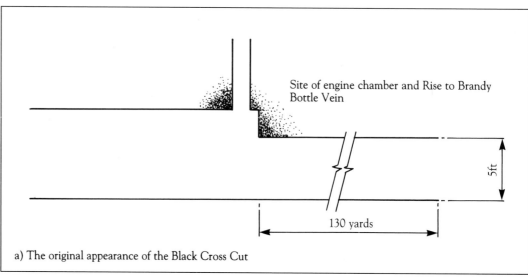

Site of engine chamber and Rise to Brandy Bottle Vein

5ft

130 yards

a) The original appearance of the Black Cross Cut

could be, and reasoned that it must have some connection with North Rake Vein, for it was not far removed from it. Two years were to elapse before we returned to the Black Cross Cut, and by this time my brother was pointing to evidence suggesting that the shaft which was almost blocking it near to the small chamber was a rise on to Brandy Bottle Vein above. We were able to confirm that this was the case, and the matter has already been discussed.

Up to this time, I had always believed that there was a step up in the Black Cross Cut between the water-filled and dry sections. This was largely due to the fact that at this place we rose five feet out of the water and could then stand to our full height. The idea was also fostered by the statement that I had read which said that Frederick Hall had installed a pump in the Fryerfold Vein to pump water up into the Black Cross Cut. My brother contested the notion that a step existed here, and a study of the area confirmed his viewpoint.

The rise of five feet was caused by our climbing up the spoil that nearly blocked the level which had spewed from the nearby rise. All of this was obvious enough, but whilst surviving in such an atrocious environment the detachment necessary to reach such a conclusion was not easily attained.

It is a matter of fact that 130 yards from the Northern end of the Black Cross Cut, the level rises suddenly in height from five to 12 feet, which seemed rather strange. About 750 of its 880 yards was driven in shale as a horse level, the remainder being five feet in height and in limestone. Raistric and Jennings speak of a part of the cross cut being smaller than a horse level. I found it most puzzling that such a long level should be driven for the better part of its length suitable for the use of horses, only finally to be reduced to the size of a drift and merely to have, as suggested, the function of a drain.

It does appear, however, that Hall had no plans to transport ore from the Fryerfold Vein via the Black Cross Cut, hence the small section of the level that was never enlarged. It is indeed made clear to us as we have already noted that he had other transport objectives for the Fryerfold Vein associated with his activities in completing the Brandy Bottle Incline.

A study of the drill marks in the level walls make it clear that 750 yards of the cross cut was driven from South to North, the remaining 130 yards being cut from the opposite end. The two sections of the level met in the vicinity of the chamber and rise at about 130 yards. Hall seems to have elected to drive the cross cut above the Hard Level Network in order to achieve greater driving speed in rock that would be more responsive to the drills. The fact that it was completed during his period of management with the Old Gang Company represents a notable achievement, but I suspect not without an unpleasant cost.

All the physical evidence in the mine points to the cross cut sloping too steeply and hence misaligning with the Fryerfold Vein, making the installation of the pump necessary in order to keep the level free of water. Faulty surveying is not usually associated with Hall, but it is a conclusion that is hard to resist. Some idea of the extent of the error can be gauged when we note that the water depth at the foot of the Brandy Bottle Incline is three feet less than that 130 yards away where the low and high sections of the level meet.

I carried out a thorough examination of the small chamber. It was largely filled with water and contained a large amount of debris. It was clear from this investigation that it was much deeper than I had thought, and I think almost certainly the site of the steam pump installed by Hall. We did wonder if, after the pump had been removed, it had later been used as a horse stable. It was certainly large enough. After it had been removed, of course, the small section of the cross cut would have flooded. It would have been uncomfortable for miners who wore only clogs to walk through.

Old tubs in the Black Cross Cut suggesting its use as an important transport highway.

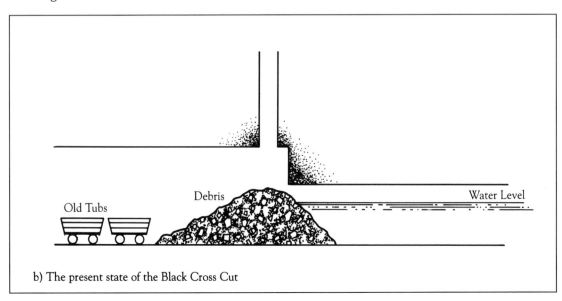

b) The present state of the Black Cross Cut

The installation of the pump was to ensure that the foot of the incline was free of water so that it would not hinder the proposed transport activities that were planned in connection with the Fryerfold Vein. Since the successors of Hall, as we know, had no interest in the incline and its transport function, they had no use for the engine and hence it was withdrawn.

We did aspire to climb into Deans Vein, but such a project was quickly realised to be beyond us for a number of reasons. With the aid of our miner's lamps we discovered that the rise was much higher than we anticipated, and this is not to mention the virtually impossible problem of transporting our equipment to the work site.

On a previous visit, I had noticed an abundance of round stones, small and large, and determined to collect some samples. They proved to be nodules which I believe contained a variety of minerals. I took particular notice of the broad gauge railway which can clearly be seen stretching for much of the length of the cross cut. When we reached the exit hole just above North Rake Vein Cross Cut, with our improved lighting we were able to see the vein. In black beds, it was clearly visible with lead much in evidence. Before us were two tunnels that had run-in. The one to the right seemed to both go on and upward, suggesting a rise. The other to the left appeared to be an extension of the cross cut, and we decided that it must have gone on implying that we had not been able to progress along the whole of it.

We climbed down into North Rake Vein in Hard Level and examined it as it travelled eastward. There was the flooded level opposite to us. The flood marks on the wall showed that the water level sometimes rose by five feet. We were looking at North Rake Vein Level which, as previously reported, has totally collapsed in at its eastern end, permitting only a small volume of water to escape. In periods of flooding the water level is kept in check as it syphons away down North Rake Vein Cross Cut. To the left of the level at North Rake but up in the dry was another working, and close to it a huge boulder supporting a stemple. Looking overhead I noticed tons of

The forbidding waterfilled low section of the Black Cross Cut.

rock that had fallen from a working and become jammed. It was probably this fall, along with other roof falls, that had all but blocked off North Rake Vein Cross Cut, which we now entered.

Some 20 yards into it, we critically examined the mysterious shaft that had given so much cause for thought on the previous visit. At the top of it with our powerful lights we thought we could see a railway. There was a drift in the wall about 30 feet up. Two abandoned rock drills were wedged in its walls. We were particularly interested in a large wall-like construction at the foot of the shaft, which stood just higher than a large iron tub. Rails ran over to its side and away again. All the evidence points to its having served as a reception point for ores and other materials mined above. It was lowered down the shaft, loaded into tubs and transported to the smelt mill. The shaft was about 50 feet in height and we thought it was driven on to the Black Cross Cut and we had been barred from reaching it by the run-in. We were interested that the water had been diverted out of the cross cut before running its full length, but the reason for this was to become apparent later. We wondered if it had been taken right through to Old Rake Vein but in time we were destined to learn.

The presence of the railway in the Black Cross Cut had exercised our minds a great deal. The physical evidence points to its being a major waygate for the transport of ore from the Dean and North Rake Veins. Doubtless it was also used for a time to move coal to the steam engine, which explains why so much of it was cut as a horse level. The only sensible way that horses could get into the cross cut was via the Brandy Bottle Incline which would restrict the size of the animals used, since they would have to pass through the low part of the level.

Hall left the Old Gang Company on 11th June, 1818, by which time Main Level had been driven 128 fathoms to the west of Bell Shaft. It would seem that there was a complete failure on the part of the Directors to comprehend the long term advantages of his schemes, and perhaps it was only justice that they were never destined to benefit from them.

The flooded North Rake Vein in the Hard Level.

The compressed air tank — Sir Francis Mine.

8

Sir George's Great Achievment

Sir George Denys Bart was a mining entrepreneur of great distinction, but unfortunately his achievements are only to be found on the hidden side of Swaledale, and consequently a proper recognition of his importance has been somewhat muted. He was greatly concerned about the evident signs of exhaustion of the ore veins in the Underset or Second Limestone, laid open by trials 80 to 100 years earlier in, for example, the Bunting, Priscilla and Hard Levels.

Sir George was a man of vision, and set about persuading his associates as to the importance of making a trial of the lower limestones. As the driving of such a cross cut would entail boring through some 750 fathoms of rock before the veins were reached, there was not much enthusiasm for his plans. It says much for his persuasive abilities, therefore, that he was able to get the Old Gang Company to join the Blakethwaite Company in the venture of driving the Sir Francis Level in Gunnerside Gill.

In July of 1864, the work was at last commenced, with Joseph Cottingham leading a small team of miners. The level was to be the regulation six feet in height, four feet in width and the miners equipped with hammers, rock drills and gun powder began their long haul. At first progress seemed satisfactory at a cost of £8.5.0 per fathom, but by 1869 this had reached £10 and progress was down to a miserable ten feet per month. At this rate, there was little chance of the work being completed, and drastic action was needed.

This action was provided by Sir George, as he endeavoured to enlist the support of his associates in "the desirability of bringing the science of the 19th Century to the aid of our old jog trot notions", and he urged the adoption of a boring machine. But as he well knew, new habits and customs are not easily introduced into Swaledale. The people of the Dale had lived close to the margin of starvation for too long to contemplate drastic change without resistance. To quote Sir George, "cold water in plenty was thrown on the scheme, it was too soon, it was too risky, it would be better to let somebody else try it first". But Sir George was determined and here showed the true spirit of the mining adventurer. He accepted the full risk of introducing machinery upon himself, since the Old Gang Company could not be persuaded to join him. It was agreed that he assume the role of a subcontractor in consideration for the payment of £8.10.0 per fathom.

The flooded Sir Francis about 170 yards into the mine under the second air shaft.

After giving due consideration to these matters, which included visits to Cornwall and Greenock, he selected the McKean borer, which was to revolutionise mining in Swaledale. He connected his new machinery to a Low's double cylinder air compressor, the motive power for which was supplied by a 39 feet diameter water wheel. In January 1870 the new boring techniques were introduced, the miners driving forward with 15 holes to complete the remaining 550 fathoms to the Fryerfold Vein. Sir George had brought in an engineer to oversee the work, but his lack of skill in mining techniques was the occasion of much mirth to the miners.

Apparently one day he bored seven holes, fired each one of them seven times, used a quarter barrel of powder and scarcely produced a hand barrowful of rock. No doubt the sight of the expert engineer with egg all over his face gave immense satisfaction to the miners, but the waste occasioned by the spectacle determined Sir George to give him his marching orders as soon as the machinery was understood.

By 1872 the level had reached Botcher Gill. The keystone to the entrance of the mine bore this date, for what reason I have never been sure. After unsuccessfully experimenting with gun cotton in 1873 Sir George persuaded the miners to use dynamite, which proved an instant success and speeded progress. Amid great rejoicing, the Fryerfold Vein was cut on the 12th March 1877, 13 long years from the day the drive started. It was six feet thick and filled throughout with good large blobs of ore, giving promise of productive work both above and below the rails.

Sir George reckoned that the task of completing the cross cut with hand labour would have cost £12-14 per fathom and been economically impossible, whereas he had broken even and in doing so had opened up the Fryerfold and connected veins which extended over fifteen miles to the east and west.

The AD Company with Sir George as Managing Director had been formed in 1873 with the specific intention of working the Lower Fourth and Fifth Limestones. A sump was put down about

72 feet and the Tiplady Drift was driven on to the vein, which proved to be eight feet thick at this point. Eighty tons of ore were being produced each month, but because of the cost of raising it from the drift combined with the poor price, £13 per ton that it was fetching at the market place, Sir George was having to consider liquidating the company. After all the hard work that had been put in, such a thought was anathema to him.

Once again he had to rally support for his ideas. The company must increase its efficiency or go out of business. It was, however, completely unable to find the necessary capital to solve its problems, and he had to come to the rescue yet again. He proposed funding the developments himself to the sum of £4,500 in order that the grossly inadequate donkey engine being used to pump out the sump be replaced by hydraulic pumping and winding engines which he intended to lease to the company. Once again, Old Gang could not be persuaded to join him and share the expense involved. As a result, they forfeited the chance of exploiting the ore they had discovered beneath the Sir Francis Level in Old Gang ground, and their workings there were drowned out at the beginning of 1881.

During 1880 Sir George held a festival at Sir Francis during which there was a band, singing, speeches and much drinking, since 30 gallons of beer had been supplied. It must have been a memorable day for those fortunate enough to be there. Sadly, viewed in retrospect however, the occasion looks far more like a commemorative farewell than the breaking of a new dawn. The long shadows of the end of an era were cast over the gathering. Only the stature, prestige and acumen of Sir George was preventing the collapse of the mining operation. Whilst the people rejoiced, Sir George must have been troubled by the economic difficulties that he saw before him and with which he continually wrestled.

The Old Manger — Sir Francis Horse Level.

Inside the entrance of Sir Francis Level, commenced 1864. Fine supporting stone arching. Compressed air pipe on the wall stretches deep into the mine.

Soon after the event, for yet a second time, he saved the company from liquidation. He was an eternal optimist and full of ideas. On bargain day, 8th December 1880, eight different projects were listed involving 80 men. It was his clear intention to prove the vein down the sump, from the bottom of the Fifth Limestone up to the Tiplady Drift. He was also planning at an estimated cost of £9,000, to unwater the Blakethwaite Veins, by taking Sir Francis Level via the North and Blind Gill Veins, a distance of 1,500 fathoms. He was able to contemplate such a long drive, which he considered would take eight years, since he intended to bring air to the mine with his compressor, so obviating the need for ventilation rises.

On the 23rd February 1881 Sir George died, and with him the dynamic spirit that had fired the mining operations of Swaledale since he had taken up residence in Draycot Hall in 1851. The miners of Swaledale had lost a true friend, for their well-being and that of their families was ever in his thoughts. His end heralded the end of a great industry in Swaledale. Among mining entrepreneurs his stature is second to none, operating as he did with such skill against the background of a failing industry. The engine he so boldly installed in Sir Francis Level started up four months after his death in July and worked for about one year, until mining in the engine sump was abandoned because of the rapidly falling price of lead. The mining company that he had set up was to stagger on for almost another 25 years, but without the dynamic leadership of someone with the commitment of Sir George it was doomed, and his like was not to reappear.

Having lost the sump workings, the company were committed to extending the network into the Watersykes Vein, which did not prove particularly bountiful in depth, and the mining operation clearly missed the strong hand of Sir George at the helm.

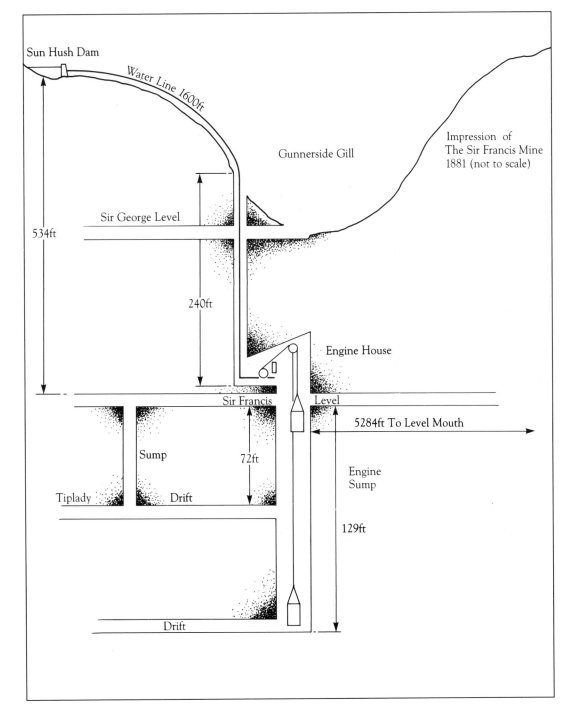

The parting of the ways in the Sir Francis Level. To the left the air pipe travels on into the AD Mines. The Old Gang Mines to the right.

53

In July of 1978, I arrived with my brother at the entrance of the Sir Francis mine. Because of some reconstruction work that had taken place in the preceding years, it had been possible to enter the mine at the entrance and walk all the way up the cross cut, but on this occasion it seemed totally blocked. After inspecting the surface, however, we found that there was just enough room to squeeze through a gap and drop down into the level. After a reconnaissance, my brother reported deep water, saying that the compressed air pipe attached to the mine wall was submerged. I realised that this could mean water at chest height, a discouraging factor. Nevertheless, we prepared for a possible expedition, abandoning some of our equipment so that we could travel light. As we gazed into the crystal clear water, we apprehensively debated whether we should proceed. Finally we made the plunge, gasping with the shock effect of the cold.

We started the mile long trek to the engine house, a task made more difficult by the plastic bags containing our photographic gear, that we endeavoured to keep above the water. We continued to wade for about half a mile in the wretched conditions. I experienced moments of acute depression as we squelched on toward the engine house, feeling under the water for the compressed air pipe. As on previous occasions, at various points water poured from the roof. I hardly dared stop to consider what I was doing and trudged on, occasionally winging a prayer heavenward.

It seemed an eternity before the water level dropped, and soon we were at the old manger, which no doubt had proved a welcome stopping place for many a horse. We rushed through a twisting low section where the compressed air pipe had fallen from the wall, scrambled over the big fall and shortly after we saw the old cage hanging above the sump at the end of a finely constructed barrel vault, witnessing to the considerable skills possessed by the old masons of Swaledale. We quickly ascended the stairway into the engine house, with difficulty lit our sodden candles and ate a bar of nut toffee.

Our spirits revived, and we were soon preoccupied with taking photographs. Sometimes our flash gun failed us. Such an event was the occasion of bitter frustration and hard to embrace, particularly after enduring considerable privations. We looked through the clear water of the engine sump commenced 100 years earlier, and could see the rope descending to meet the cage 130 feet below. We were glad to be off to make the return journey to bank. After having taken a photograph of the manger, we hastened on down the level, spurred on by the thought that at the end of the journey was light and the joy of being in the open once more. At one point, we heard a dull thud, and must conclude that something had fallen, making a most alarming noise. Many fathoms back in the mine, I saw the first wan wisp of light. One was tempted to charge forward, always a mistake, for such uncontrolled behaviour on a previous occasion had cost me my

The Pumps, Sir Francis Mine.

One hundred year old platforms supporting tons of rubble left behind by miners in Sir Francis Level.

photographs. It had taken us one hour to come down the level, and the whole trip had been accomplished in five hours. We scrambled through the narrow crack into Gunnerside Gill. There was a stiff wind blowing and it had been raining. The conditions were uninviting, but compared to the previous five hours we were in paradise. As we trudged up the fell, with the wind cutting in our faces and the rain gently falling, I felt a sense of relief born of the belief that I was not to pass this way again.

In the event, this proved not to be the case. As 1981 came nearer, I began to feel compelled to register some recognition of the one hundredth anniversary of Sir George's death. One final visit to the engine house was called for. Never before had I experienced such a trouble free journey. My brother and I entered the mine, descending Staple Shaft on a lovely summer day. There were two such shafts at the beginning of the Sir Francis, and I believe them to have been put in to give access and air to the mine whilst the masons were strengthening the first few fathoms. They were, in effect, service shafts.

Using the simple system that we had developed for transporting our photographic equipment where water was a problem, we experienced little difficulty in negotiating the level. The level passes through several veins. Shortly after entering the water at the second air shaft, there is the Dougill String. This is followed by the Barbara and Watersykes Veins, a trial having been attempted at the latter. When we reached Fryerfold Vein where the mine divided between the Old Gang and A.D. Ground, we began to observe very closely.

Ore had been won at this point, and no doubt this was the strike that had occasioned so much pleasure to all concerned in 1877. A string was discovered close to the Fryerfold Vein, and the platforms erected 100 years earlier still bore the tons of rock placed on them by the miners. One day these platforms will break under the weight of the tons of rock that they hold, and falling they will probably block the level and shut off the engine house forever. The photograph that I took here sums up the whole position. Sir George and the A.D. Company were committed to the use of new technology, whereas the Old Gang Company continued with the less risky old ways. Significantly, ten years later the Old Gang Company ceased to exist. We thoroughly inspected the engine house machinery, which was most impressive. I reflected that it would be working and the engine house a hive of activity 100 years earlier. Now, here, the apple of Sir George's eye and his hope of watering out the lower levels lay entombed and silent, a monument to his determination and enterprise.

It was not difficult to imagine this place alive with the noise of work, peopled with men often worried over insecure wages and employment prospects. Taking one last look around this now desolate place, we finally departed, leaving the engine to the ghost of the Old Man.

The old winding engine, Sir Francis mine.

The cage over the old engine sump.

View from Bunting looking up towards Blakethwaite.

9

The End of a Great Industry

The Roman Legions defeated the Brigantes near Gilling in about AD 74, and we know, from the discovery of certain pigs of lead, that they engaged in mining activities in Swaledale. But there is evidence to suggest that the origins of the industry go back even further than the Romans. It has been argued that there are evidences of an Egyptian presence in the dale and the intriguingly named Hartlakes situated between Kisdon and Beldi Hill has been identified as the possible site of a foundry used by Egyptian metallurgists conscripted in the service of their state some 5,000 years before Christ. It is clear that the lead mining industry in Swaledale can boast great antiquity and at its zenith it employed something like 4,000 men, not to mention women and children.

Old hopper, Watersykes Vein, Priscilla Level.

Levels of activity across the centuries varied according to slump or boom periods, but toward the end of the 19th Century, in 1871, the Bewick Report to the Directors of the Old Gang Mining Company was sounding a sombre note. It reads, "Comparing these easternmost workings in Watersykes Vein (at present and for some time past, almost the only part of the field yielding ore), with what they were at my last and preceding inspections, there are not any good grounds for congratulation". The signs that the upper ore beds were close to exhaustion, spurred Sir George Denys Bart as we have already noted to undertake the driving of the Sir Francis Level, to expose ore bearing ground in the lower limestones.

A great depression occurred in the 1880's, and in the years 1880-82 many mines closed down. In 1884 Sir Francis Denys Bart was advised that it had been necessary to stop ore getting in the Old Gang, and several trials were recommended that might be sensibly pursued by the 'dead men', that is the non-productive mine workers. In those mines struggling to remain open the miners were earning starvation wages. Despite the recommendation to Sir Francis, the ore getting in Old Gang appears to have continued to some extent, for pickmen are recorded as earning 9/- per week in the mid 80's, and things were so bad by 1887 that miners were leaving the A.D. Company, being on the point of starvation.

Mining companies in Arkengarthdale fared rather better at this time, since they were still able to work more productive veins and show a modest profit. It is rather ironic that during these dreadful times a Factory Inspector was writing threatening letters to the Agent of the A.D. Mines, because of a failure to comply with certain paperwork procedures.

The seriousness of the times is underlined by the population losses experienced in Melbecks Swaledale, the area in which the Old Gang Mine was situated. Between 1871-91, the population fell by 58%, whilst in Reeth the school lost more than half the children on the register in the year 1882.

Another interesting piece of evidence concerning the decline of the lead mines is to be found in the lead production figures of the Old Gang Mine, used as evidence to promote a railway in Swaledale.

1874/78	5233 tons
1879/83	2965 tons
1884/88	906 tons
1889/94	320 tons (1567 tons of lead ore).

Statistics such as these conceal a mountain of misery. There was nothing to cushion the people in their distress such as we know today. Temporary Short Time Working and Reduncancy Payments were to be aids for those of the distant future. Many of the miners were forced to dig up their roots and go elsewhere, to the textile mills of Lancashire, the coal mines of Durham, or even further afield to the land of opportunity, America. In the 1880's the A.D. Company was heavily in debt, and during 1887 the Old Gang Company gave up the unequal struggle and surrendered its lease. This led to the formation of the Old Gang Lead Mining Company Limited, promoted to work the combined A.D.—Old Gang areas, but the venture was attended with little success. The social disturbance at this time must have been enormous. Throughout the dale, large numbers of houses had been deserted, shops and pubs closed, whilst teachers salaries slumped as school rolls plummeted.

In January 1904 miners led by William Buxton started to drive the last rise between the Sir Francis and Priscilla Levels. it was very costly, being completed in April 1905 and the men were drenched to the skin as they worked. In March of 1904, a violent explosion took place about 70 feet up causing much alarm, but fortunately claimed no casualties. After the rise had been started, it was realised that it would be premature. Lead ore was found in Priscilla Soles, but it could not be extracted to any extent, because the rise could only drain it for a few fathoms. Although the price of lead was rising at this time, the company was drained of capital and could not engage in an expensive trial, that would require the Sir Francis Horse level to be driven forward and a new rise put up.

It was something of a tragedy that the end had to come in this way, since the strata beds were dipping toward Sir Francis, which was ideally placed to exploit them, and it was perfectly clear that ore was there for the getting, as Simpson Eales productive working in Priscilla Soles, a drift forward of the Sir Francis in the Underset Chert was drowned out in January 1901. So it was then, that Sir George's dream of unwatering the Blakethwaite Veins with the Sir Francis Level died, with the forehead some 780 fathoms short of the objective.

Pressed by Sir Francis Denys Bart, the Company went into liquidation in October 1906. There was very little successful mining in Swaledale after this, since it had become increasingly clear that there were no appreciable loads of lead to be found below the Underset Limestone, although some work in Arkengarthdale continued for a few years. So the curtain was drawn on a way of life, and generations of mining history faded away.

*　　　*　　　*

In July 1980, my brother and I approached Blind Gill, with little enthusiasm or hope of success. The wild hope was that we might gain access to Priscilla Level down one of the several rises in that mine, and from thence descend Buxton's Rise to the forehead of Sir Francis level. The easiest route to Priscilla would be via Cyprian Rutter's or Frank Parker's Rise. From the very outset we knew that there was a question mark against the likelihood of success, as both the old miners had brought their rises up through the ore workings in 1900, and the odds were that their lower sections would be blocked with fallen mining spoil, thus preventing access to Priscilla.

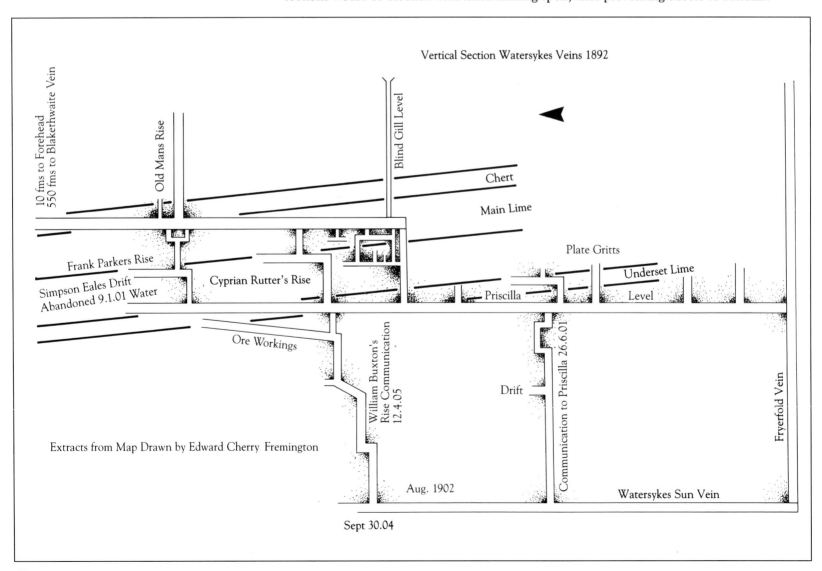

Extracts from Map Drawn by Edward Cherry Fremington

Despite our initial scepticism, the trip proved productive. We entered the level, and immediately had to struggle through thick black slime. On our first visit, we carried our equipment in the small improvised boat that we were finding so useful where it was necessary to wade through large volumes of water. The cross cut to the vein was in the shale, and the roof looked decidedly unsound in several places. On arrival at the vein, the level at first appeared to have fallen in, for before us was a mountain of rock and to the left a rise, out of which water tumbled. We clambered over the fallen rock and entered Reynoldsons Cross Cut, which had been driven some 80 fathoms on to some small veins, the whole venture having proved an expensive failure was abandoned in 1898.

Later we found it possible to squeeze through a small hole and gain access to Blind Gill Vein. It had obviously been very rich, and there was evidence of ore workings both in the floor and roof. We crossed what must have been Thomas Rutter's Sump and Ore Workings, which had been excavated as late as 1900. The level had crumbled away in many places, but remarkably was accessible for 150 fathoms. After it had swung sharply to the right, we came upon what I had been anxiously looking out for, some 140 fathoms from Blind Gill Cross Cut.

Laying back from the level was Cyprian Rutters Main Rise through from Priscilla Level. When it was put in at the turn of the century, water problems proved a hazard and a dog leg was driven in the strata some 40 feet underneath Blind Gill Level. It therefore rose in two stages. Frank Parkers Rise was inaccessible, so all hopes of success were pinned on Cyp Rutter and the work that he had done 80 years earlier.

A further year was to elapse before our investigations could continue. Considerable amounts of equipment were called for, and it was floated up the level on an improvised raft. It started to rain heavily as we entered the level, and apparently continued to do so all the time we were in the mine. It was 2 p.m., far too late to be starting a task of this magnitude, which required just the two of us to walk our heavy load several miles across the moor, and at the entrance to the mine, drag ourselves through the thick stinking sludge.

After perseverance the craft began to float and slow progress was made up the 1,320 yards to the vein. On reaching it, we quickly ascertained that little had changed and the equipment was disembarked. A loose rail that been earmarked for use was still there. My brother went to investigate that Cyp Rutters Rise was still accessible, whilst I began the arduous chore of moving the equipment up to the scene of operations, a task not made easier by the sump workings in the floor.

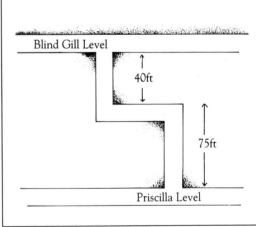

Cyprian Rutter's Main Rise, Blind Gill Mine.

It was interesting to see how water now escaped from the mine, since it lay three and a half feet deep in the cross cut, and water from the stream in Blind Gill actually entered it at the mouth. It travels 20 yards down the level where the vein joins the cross cut and disappears through the floor into some Old Man's workings. These are connected to a rise from Priscilla down which it falls, and finally makes its way to daylight through Sir Francis Mine.

My brother suddenly appeared out of the gloom, indicating that everything was 'go' for our attempt to descend the rise. In making our preparations for the descent, we discovered that it was going to be necessary to support the rail with iron stakes. We had brought some with us, but had left them at the cross cut. Reluctantly, but in the interests of safety, I returned to the cross cut to collect four small irons, and on the return journey stumbled on putting my foot into a water-filled sump that had largely been filled with deads. I went headlong in the mud, but arrived back at the rise with nothing more than a graze to show for my mishap. We were still not satisfied with the security of the rail and this time my brother returned to the cross cut to collect two long irons. He seemed gone for an eternity, and I busied myself taking photographs.

Finally the iron rail was secure, and we set about the task of lowering our ladder. It was not easy, as the rungs often caught at narrow points. I was the first down, but was very disappointed to find at

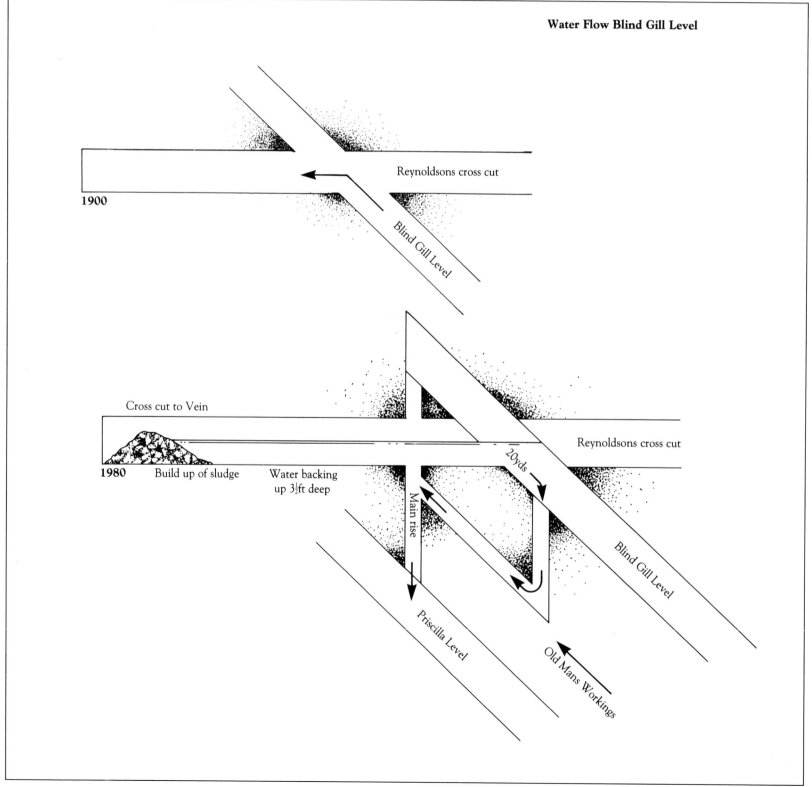

Water Flow Blind Gill Level

Reynoldsons cross cut

1900

Blind Gill Level

Cross cut to Vein

Reynoldsons cross cut

20yds

1980   Build up of sludge   Water backing
up 3½ft deep

Main rise

Blind Gill Level

Priscilla Level

Old Mans Workings

about 30 feet the rise had become a dumping ground for deads, and there was no chance of our getting to the dog leg, let alone to the Sir Francis via Priscilla. The rise could be seen going on down, but it was quite impassable.

I returned to the top, and my brother descended. He noticed a small drift in the wall which he succeeded in entering, but had great difficulty in leaving since he was cut off from the ladder. From the top, with the aid of our rope, I was able to assist him to climb to safety. The small drift appeared to be nothing more than a convenient place to store equipment, and the only thing found in it was a small detonator box.

The reduction of the level to resume regulation height. The top of the choked level can be seen in the middle of picture.

Photographs were taken, but it was very late when we got back to the cross cut. The raft was packed as quickly as conditions would allow, and we set off on our long slow journey to the entrance. The rain that had fallen continually did not affect the mine whilst we were there, but its impact would certainly be felt some hours later, as experience had taught us. Toward the entrance, we had to 'cuff' ourselves in the stinking mud again, and left the mine at 9 p.m. We had promised our wives that we would 'phone them at this hour, and here we were miles from anywhere, standing in the failing light, drenched with rain up to our eyes in stenching filth. There was nothing that we could do about it, but we were aware of the consternation that we would cause to others, and on top of this our mission had seemed a total failure.

As we made our way up the moor, our mood was one of deep depression. How could a rise that had been put up at the turn of the century be full of deads, I wondered. Two days later, with great difficulty, we were able to make a deep penetration of Priscilla Level. At about 340 fathoms along North Vein out toward the Great Break, we came upon a significant fall out. I expected a build up of water behind it, but there was none. I thought therefore that there would be a rise not far away, and sure enough almost immediately it was upon us. Water was still draining into it, despite its being full of deads. Presumably it went down via Sir George to the Sir Francis level. A few yards further on our progress was halted. The floor had been ripped out, leaving a gaping hole barring the way to the Great Break, and unwanted rock from this excavation had doubtless been tossed into the rise to save the long haul back to bank in Gunnerside Gill.

Intriguing masonry and wooden supports, Watersykes Vein, Priscilla Level.

It was then that the events of our failed visit to Blind Gill began to take on meaning. The miners had ripped the Blind Gill Mine to shreds in their search for lead, and in their deepening financial crisis adopted short term solutions to their problems which destroyed the mine, as the old disciplines associated with former profitable mining operations were no longer observed. It was not therefore surprising to find that Cyp Rutters Rise, driven only a few years earlier, had become a dumping ground for unwanted waste.

As I looked upon the desecration of Priscilla Level, it appeared to me that the miners had combined in a corporate act of vandalism against the mines. No doubt they wished to profit by pockets of ore that they knew or hoped were in the floor, and carried out excavations near rises to solve their transport problems. The last days in Priscilla betrayed all the hallmarks of desperation. Things are known to have been desperate at the end, they must have been desperate indeed!

An old arch withstands the collapse of the level around it. Blind Gill Mine.

It seems that the basic necessities of good mining practice were sacrificed in the frantic search for a living. The same practices mentioned here were perpetrated in other mines and were undoubtedly responsible for the blocking of the rise from the George to Bunting levels, the discovery of which occasioned so much disappointment a year earlier. The digging out of the soles of levels and the blocking of rises appeared to be common practice in Swaledale when the death of a mining operation seemed imminent, or perhaps may already have taken place. We found evidence of these practices in Whitaside, Moulds and the Sun Gutter Mines, as well as Old Gang.

There would have been nothing to prevent the miners re-routing levels in order to extract ore without destroying the basic structure of the mine. Clearly there was no time for such obvious adjustments to be made and the money was not available to pay for them. So after generations, the mines were gradually abandoned, and in the case of Priscilla, good ore was left in the soles, and the same could almost certainly be said for Blakethwaite.

So the curtain had fallen on a great industry that had made work opportunities for miners, carpenters, masons, quarrymen and smiths to name but a few, and it would appear that the mines and the miners perished together.

Smithy Level.

10

A Brief Encounter

The year was 1954, and I was on my way to Gunnerside to take up the post of the last of a long line of young Methodist Ministers in Swaledale. It had all started several generations before when William Buxton, a devout lead miner, had discovered a goodly strike of lead ore. For his hard labours he received what was then a princely sum which he determined to use for the building of Gunnerside's first Methodist Chapel which was completed in 1789. The existing chapel replaced it in 1867 and now all these years later my role was to bring spiritual comfort to those distinctive people, whose forebears had for generations been miners. They had weathered the trauma of the death of the mining industry, but their particular way of living remained relatively untouched by outside influences. There was a reasonable bus service, and the private car had still not taken hold. The tractor was just beginning to make its appearance, and an occasional television was to be found, but the dale still had its small, tightly knit village communities, that as yet had not been infiltrated by invading town dwellers. The Chapel still had a substantial influence, although this had waned somewhat during the course of the century.

Each year, the Mid Summer Festival would see the return of former villagers who had been forced to leave in search of work elsewhere. There was no shortage of preachers who relished the honour of being invited to conduct the service on this auspicious occasion. So important an event was it, I recall, that the householders would scrub the tops of walls and doorsteps, and have the village looking 'as bright as a new halfpenny'.

Like all communities, Swaledale had its fair share of individuals who were unable to resist the temptations of the flesh or the lure of the bottle, and I recall that the bush telegraph was always very swift, but somewhat careless about the facts. As a newcomer to the dale, I would normally have been subject to a long period of probation lasting several years before being accepted, but for the minister this probationary period was waived, and I was generously and openheartedly accepted at once.

The people of Swaledale were independent and strong minded. They were not without generosity, but managed their money carefully, a habit born of an uncertain income expectation from mining. During my pastoral visits to homes in the villages and outlying farms I was always pressed to have 'a cup of tea'. I soon learned that 'a cup of tea' involved a clean table cloth and numerous cakes and buns, almost always delicious and home made. It was sort of expected that I would say "Yes," to these invitations, and if I made several visits during an afternoon my gastronomic powers were severely tested!

After living one year in Gunnerside I was required to move on, and it was with great reluctance that I departed from a people whose lives were so influenced by a simple expression of Christianity, and whose devotion to the family ideal compelled admiration. Thirty years on, this way of living which I was privileged to share with them so briefly, has now largely disappeared. The Dales are increasingly occupied by a new tribe of incomers, and literally dozens of cottages once inhabited by the offspring of former miners are now relegated to the role of second homes and holiday cottages.

I regret that I did not show any particular interest in the miners during my brief sojourn in Swaledale, for there were many alive then who could have supplied me with valuable intelligence but, thankfully, years later sources of information were still to be found. I was much saddened on hearing early in 1983 of the death of my old friend Mrs. L. Herring. In the now rapidly receding days when I ministered to the people of Gunnerside she proved to be something of a mother to me, possessing the characteristic Yorkshire bluntness, along with a wonderful sense of humour and an outstandingly generous spirit. Because of her great longevity she could still cast her mind back to that era when the mines still functioned as a powerful force, and through her I could, as it were, still reach men who had long since been dead.

Her father, Thomas Sunter, a relative of my wife's family, like his father before him was a miner and worked at the Old Gang, travelling there daily from Bank Heads, Crackpot. He acquired a small property there for the sum of £400 in the 1890's. Perhaps it is a commentary on our own times that the same property changed hands for, I understand, something in the region of £48,000 in the early 1980's, not far short of a 12,000% increase in price. Sometimes in the winter the cold

Main rise from Low to Smithy Level.

was so intense, Mr. Sunter used to joke, that his trousers froze on him and when he took them off they were capable of standing up on their own. In those days they used to cover porridge with straw to keep it warm, and there was no tea so they drank mash mallow made from a local flower. The men and women of the villages met in one another's homes to converse and knit, whilst miners would make their candles from tallow.

There were no social workers to call upon then, the community being organised on a self help basis. Despite the harshness of the times, there was no lack of compassion for the needy. The young people, Mrs. Herring reminded me, used to be called in to sit with and comfort the ageing and sick.

Hunger was a constant spectre, not alleviated by the 3s. 6d. that could be obtained through the Work House, but no one was allowed to starve. She remembered that her mother sustained four old women with constant gifts of dairy produce, and in the same vein my wife's grandfather, John Jackson, often forgave hard pressed families the debts they had run-up for much needed boots and clothing, and he was known to accept a sheep in lieu of cash. It was through the many acts of this nature that the people of the dale were able to weather the economic blizzards that raged around them.

Mr. Sunter kept three cows whilst he worked as a miner, but he later obtained the tenancy of Lonsdale Broderick's farm at Spring End, and so he escaped from the mines and lived to the ripe old age of 88. It is well known that Lonsdale Broderick was not a Christian and the Church ostracised his funeral when he was buried in unconsecrated ground. Mr. Sunter, a local preacher, played his part in the funeral arrangements, and I suspect that he drew upon his old mining skills to blast the grave in the hard rock on the lonely hill above Spring End, where Mr. Broderick had requested that he be laid to rest.

Mrs. Herring recalled how some of the miners set a man trap in the Kinning Mine, to ensnare a fellow miner with whom they had a grievance. The reason for the tension she could not recall, but perhaps he was suspected of stealing ore from his peers, always considered a most heinous crime. When they entered the mine the following morning, their adversary was already dead. Harsh justice we may think, but that is how it was in those days.

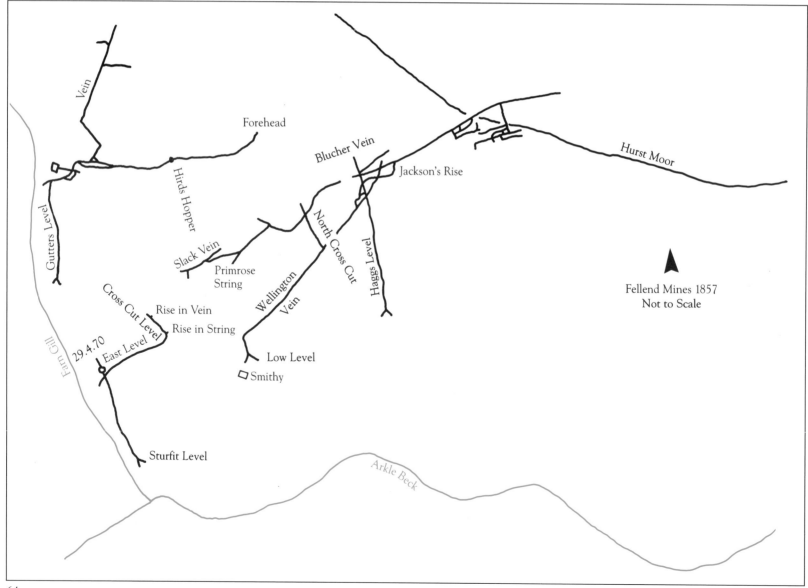

She could remember Cyp Rutter, Frank Parker, Simpson Eales and Bill Buxton, all of whom had worked for the A.D. Company, but the miner who had left the most abiding impression upon her was George Rutter. He was a preacher of some distinction in his day. "Bye, we'd go anywhere to hear him," she said, recalling his distinctive mannerism, that of putting his thumbs in his waistcoat pockets as he held his congregation spellbound, whilst he preached the Gospel.

Years later his son Willie, a retired schoolmaster, used to deliver my milk. He had a great sense of humour, and I am indebted to him for this story of a miner who had been converted to Christianity during an upsurge of religious fervour. His lack of learning was fully exposed at one service he was conducting because he had chosen as his scripture reading that difficult passage from Daniel chapter 3 which rehearses several times a whole list of instruments of music, including the harp, the sackbut, the psaltery and dulcimer. Whilst reading his lesson to the congregation he stumbled as best he could through the list of instruments. Shortly after, when confronted with the same list again he said,

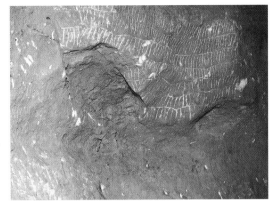

The ore tally, Whitaside Mine.

"Hello, I am not going to say this again, but it's the same band playing!"

Over in Arkengarthdale in 1904, at the age of 50, James Harker gratefully left the mines for the last time. He was working in the Stang Mine, and used to emerge out of Hurr Gill Shaft and walked across the moor to the Barnard Castle road. He had combined mining with working a small holding at Booze, but now he was to devote himself entirely to farming at Watson House.

During his long career as a miner he had worked in Faggergill Mine, and at that time for several months of the year he never saw daylight, for after walking two miles to the mine he had a journey of two miles underground by candle light to reach his work station. He participated in the driving of Haggs Level and also worked in the Windeg Mines.

Always there was the desperate urgency to make a living, fair and foul means being used to achieve that end. A band of miners blasting their way under Spanham Moor came on to virgin ground containing good ore that they had no right to mine, but this did not prevent them from robbing it. We are indebted to James Harker for this titbit of information, and I suspect that he may have been one of these miners, although with something of a twinkle in his eye, his son Joseph could not confirm it!

A miners record of the opening out of a level, 1811 Gorton Mine.

We have already noted that the miner had to guard against being robbed by other colleagues, and to give him some warning if theft was afoot, James Harker used to string a fine strand of cotton across a working which of course would not be seen, and could be easily broken without anyone being the wiser.

James Harker had followed his father into the mines, and he was determined that his son should not labour as he had done in the bowels of the earth. "Whatever thu dus," he advised, "Keep sky for thee roof," words not forgotten by young Joseph, who never set foot in a mine. Recalling the frantic search of the old people for security, he reminded me that, "There was nobut lead paid in them days," and the driving of a cross cut was tersely dismissed with the words, "They spent a lot of time for nowt".

There were occasions during our wanderings underground that we felt a special closeness to the old miners. Our first visit to Eldorado is perhaps the most outstanding memory, but there are others. In 1981 we spent two days climbing a hopper under Bunting Hush near to the Miller Cross Cut. The vein in the horse level looked most unpromising, but by resolutely following it the miners were to discover a most productive strike. My brother did the hard work and I merely played the support role, although the cold ate into me as I stood for hours beneath him in the horse level. The timbers in the rise were quite rotten, so using our irons he tortuously hammered his way upward. It was a brilliant piece of climbing for one who had not been trained in such techniques, and by the end of the day he was exhausted, having almost reached the drift at the top of the rise. We started work early next morning, and after securing two more irons he was into the drift. It went on about 60 yards to a large stope. The rise also continued on up, following the vein which was clearly visible. We remembered that we had seen this kind of thing before.

The miners had driven into a large ore body, and would set up their wooden platforms as they worked their way up the stope. Some of these had now collapsed in blocking the drift. They also drove the rise on up so that they could meet the vein with another drift higher up. It is probable, we believe, that this working was being used in the late 18th or very early 19th centuries.

My brother reported finding clog prints, establishing the fact that he was the first visitor to the drift since the miners left. Initially he thought it contained a small railway, but when he reported that there was the remains of an old wooden neck halter in the drift, we knew then that ore had been manhandled by human labour, probably transporting it to the hopper in wooden buckets. We had found an old wooden bucket in the Morey Vein in the Watersykes Level some years earlier. The ore would be tipped into the hopper, to be received in the horse level below. The halter had a slight semicircle in it which was consistent with buckets being transported on the stooping shoulders of miners. Feeling that he was on hallowed ground, my brother took steps not to erase the clog prints. After taking a photographic record of his surroundings he rejoined me in the horse level.

In 1982, we entered the Gorton Level, which was conveniently placed to mine the Main Limestone on the Eastern side of Bunting Beck. Several drifts went off to the right down toward the Old Rake and Fryerfold Veins. At the commencement of one of them an old miner had chiselled the date, 1811. It was a sobering thought that this drift was being opened up whilst Napoleon was invading Russia, and Wellington was conducting his successful campaign in the Iberian Peninsula. Events of this nature did not go unnoticed in Swaledale, for the Wellington and Blucher Veins give some indication of popular opinion at the defeat of Napoleon at the Battle of Waterloo in 1815.

Little incidents of this nature, we felt, gave us momentary glimpses of the old miners. Abandoned tools, footprints or marks on the wall, made us aware that years before, men in pursuit of their livelihood had passed this way.

A year earlier, we had entered Smithy Level on Whitaside. A small shaft had been cleverly dropped on to it by someone possessing mining skills. Without the exercise of these skills we are mindful that we could never have entered several of the mines, and we are indebted to those who have been of such great help to us. About 700 yards into the mine, we entered a small drift that had been cut in Sandstone. There were clog prints clearly visible in the dry floor, creating an eerie impression within us. We took steps not to erase them, although the following year they were gone, rubbed out by other visitors. We came on to what at first we thought was a sump in the floor of a small drift. Above our heads was a rise on to an important working. Close at hand were scratchings on the wall where a miner had tallied ore that had been passed to him. Investigation showed that the sump was in fact a rise from a lower level, which had been used as a dump for unwanted deads. The drift on the other side of the sump had been pushed forward several yards, before it came to an end. Was it a late unsuccessful trial where, as was so often the case, the rises were used to obviate the need for transport?

On reflection, the tally marks on the wall related to loads of ore passed down from the stope above. It was then probably brought out to Smithy Main Horse Level, or alternatively lowered down the shaft to the level below.

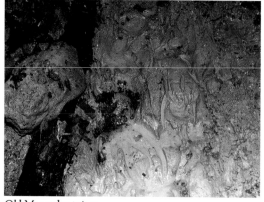

Old Mans clog prints.

We squeezed our way out of this mine into a glorious sunlit evening. As we turned our back upon it, all we had for company was a pewit whose plaintive cry sought to lure us from its nest, whose whereabouts we knew not, and for which we had no concern.

During a week in which we had been cut off from the world, our cities had erupted in violence and disorder. The crisis of our time would have been well understood by the people of Swaledale, although they were forced to meet a situation involving some similarities somewhat differently.

Perhaps we should allow the last word to Joseph Harker. Talking to him of the frantic efforts of the last miners to make a living and the wholesale destruction that we had found in the mines, he observed with his own way of life in mind, "You have to live first, before you can farm. If you can't mak it a go, summuts going to go". Here was an old man, who had received the most rudimentary education, telling me that primary needs must first be satisfied before a fuller life could be enjoyed. He had discovered in the university of life what others had spent years studying and verifying in university laboratories.

It would seem that 100 years after the signs were evident of a major collapse of the mines, the societies that they sustained with their distinctive ways, like the miners before them, have disappeared and we are the poorer for their passing.

A shot of a vein the miners were following.

Vein in the wall near the Miller Cross Cut.

Looking down Old Man's Rise to Bunting Horse Level. The Vein is visible in the right hand wall of the rise.

Fremie Hutchinson and Harold Brown.

11

The Last Witness

I had always known that if I was to do justice to a study of this nature, I would have to meet Fremie Hutchinson. He was born in 1910, the son of Fremont Hutchinson, one of the old men who worked the last shift in the Faggergill Mine in November 1911 with the Stang and Cleasby Mining Company. In the 1890's, when the Swaledale Mines were showing ominous signs of failure, some members of the Hutchinson Family, seeking a greater degree of security, emigrated to America. They took up residence in a French settlement called Fremont and gave this name to a son born there. To their great sorrow he died, and they requested the family back in Swaledale to take up the name, and in this manner Fremie's father was named. He passed the name on to his son, and he has been called 'Fremie' by the natives of Swaledale ever since.

Of all the people that I have spoken to, he possesses a unique position. Not only was he the son of an old lead miner, he was also a miner himself, and worked along with his father in the Fremington Chert Mines for many years. For a time he was the licensee of the Tan Hill Inn, and whilst he lived in this remote place he mined his own coal. Of necessity, he would have an intimate knowledge of the techniques and terminology of the Old Man.

Moulds Level. Once a great mine, providing a link with the Sir Francis Mine in Gunnerside Gill.

I particularly questioned him on how a rise was put up within a mine. It appears they drove them upward in two halves. One half would be covered by a platform, to give the miners protection. The rock that had been blasted with dynamite was knocked out and put down the other half of the rise to be carried away. The drills were put in at an angle, never straight, and whenever he used his hammer in driving upward he brought it through his legs. He noted that it was easier drilling upward than along, because the dust always fell out of the hole in the one case, but had to be removed in the other. He said that it was usual to drive forward by taking out the bottom part of the level first. It appears that the average progress in driving would be made at the rate of one yard per day, and he remembered that Plate was a particularly tough and dusty rock to drill through. When the old miners inform us on their maps that they put in a plug, this merely tells us that they stopped driving forward but might return to do so if it seemed to be to their advantage.

Fremie took part in the last trial for lead in Swaledale during the later years of the 1939-45 war. The miners cleared out the Prize Level at Hurst and came upon a most impressive working, all arched, something like a cathedral. There was a large sump there filled with water, and there was evidence that the location once housed a pump. The miners drove the level forward in Plate and put in a rise finding traces of lead, but they knew that the Old Man had 'sniffed out' the lead down the sump and they did not possess the capital or equipment to pump it out.

The Old Man wore no helmets and had to rely on candles as his only source of light. The naked flame of the candle was an important means of warning to the miner in the old days. If the flame went down, he knew that he must get out of that place immediately. Fremie recalled that such a thing once happened to him whilst he was working with Nigel Hutchinson in the Prize Level. Their lights nearly went out, and they were subject to dizziness and headaches.

"Come on", said Fremie, "we're off, because if we don't, we'll never get out of here."

They could not work in this particular place until the following morning, because they had blasted the air out of the workings.

Fremie was the last man to ship a load of lead out of Swaledale in 1948. He found an exposed vein on Fell Moor End and followed it. It yielded about three tons of lead before it ran out, for which he received £110 per ton. He has no doubt that with investment the vein could have been found again, but it was beyond him to do these things on his own. The price that he received for his lead compared favourably with my stipend as a Methodist Minister in 1955 of £189 per annum. In addition to this, I might add, I was living in rent free accommodation.

The last agent bar one in Arkengarthdale was William Peacock and he had declared that he would open the dale out, and make it a prosperous mining community again. He was behind the driving of the New Level in Faggergill the keystone of which bore the date 1885. It was his intention to push the level under Cleasby Hill, confirming the strong belief that a rich ore strike is there ready for the taking. For some reason, now lost to view, William Peacock was dismissed by his employers and went to the mines in Nidderdale. Recalling the somewhat similar situation that developed between Frederick Hall and the Old Gang Lead Mining Company, was history repeating itself? Could Peacock's ambitious schemes for the proposed new developments have alarmed his directors and led to the premature termination of his contract? Alas, we shall never know!

A fascinating sequel to the dismissal of Peacock, concerned the miners working in the Windeg Mines at the time, who had just uncovered a good strike of ore. Peacock pulled these men out of the mine and the location of the lead was kept a secret from the new agent, Mr. Thomas Harker. It was in fact never worked.

I found it difficult to understand why the locaton of good ore should be kept a secret, but the truth is the old miners liked to make a bargain, receiving so much a bing (8 cwt) for the lead mined. If the agent knew that lead was present in a particular area of a mine, he would not offer such a good price to the miner for the products of his labour.

Mr. Harker, the new agent, was a prominent member of the Methodist Community. I well

Impressive double arch along Folly Vein giving access to Stemple Vein. Reveals some of the stone arching found in profusion in this level.

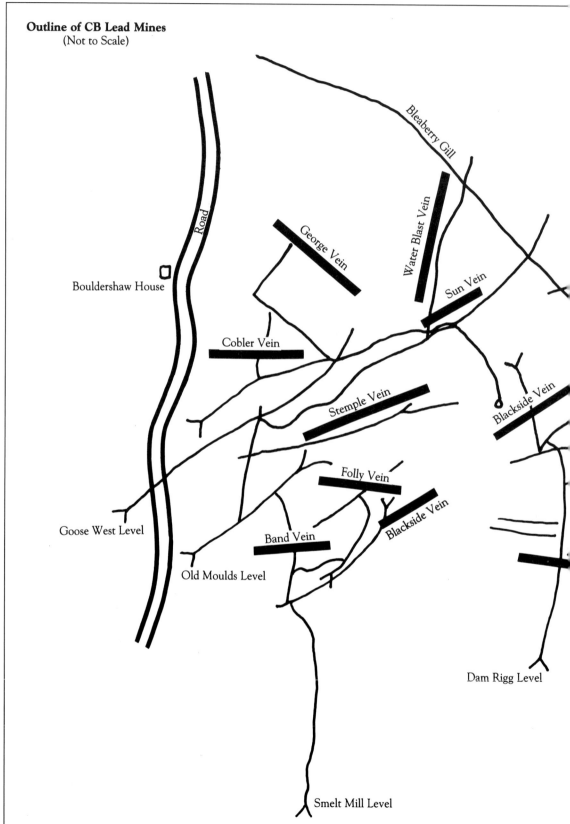

Outline of CB Lead Mines
(Not to Scale)

Bleaberry Gill

Water Blast Vein

George Vein

Sun Vein

Boul'dershaw House

Cobler Vein

Blackside Vein

Stemple Vein

Folly Vein

Goose West Level

Blackside Vein

Band Vein

Old Moulds Level

Dam Rigg Level

Smelt Mill Level

remember his son George was the organist at the Arkengarthdale Chapel during my ministry in Swaledale, and he had been one of the miners who had worked in the Nuthole Mine until it closed down.

The New level that Peacock intended to drive under Cleasby Hill was turned away to the left to follow a big joint which permitted easier driving forward. It was possible, apparently, for a miner to crawl for a considerable distance along this joint. It is quite clear to me from the conversations that I have had about this development that it was a decision which occasioned much debate and controversy within the mining community. Doubtless, as the mines staggered on ever closer to closure, the numbers who doubted the wisdom of not following Peacock's original intentions grew, although the soundness of his plans have yet to be tested.

During his period as agent, Mr. Harker almost lost his life, being trapped by a fall of rock. The prompt action of an unrelated namesake, who almost ripped his hands to shreds during the rescue, saved his life.

Large timbers snapped like twigs by earth pressures in the Moulds Level.

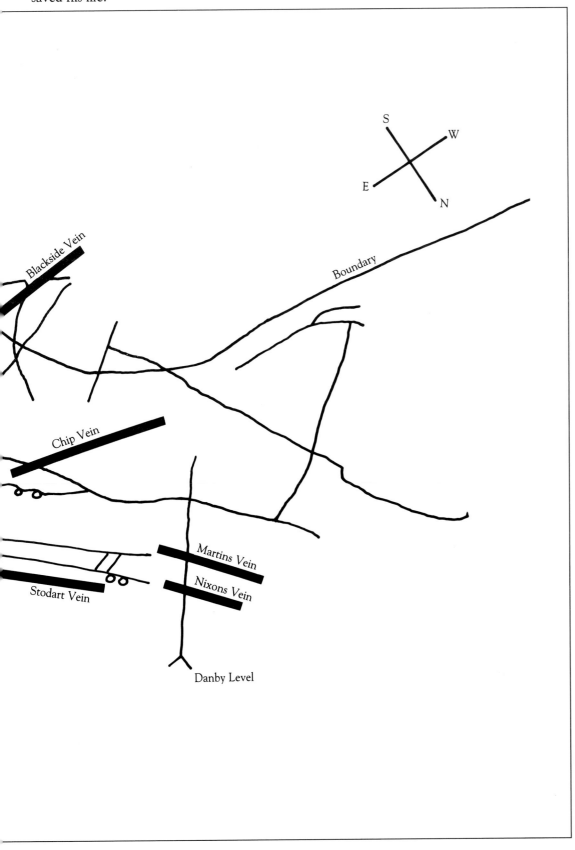

The devotion of the miners to the Methodist cause is well known, but if evidence were needed to substantiate this, it has surely been provided by Mrs. H. Batty, whose small volumes concerning the Methodists of Arkengarthdale and Gunnerside reveals them as well represented among church office holders.

Fremie paints a vivid picture of the dale still under the miner's dominion. As he remembers them, these men could be rough, having a brand of humour that might not be readily appreciated by an outsider. They would not hesitate to let off a cracker or two if it suited them, and this no doubt explains why the porch of the Red Lion at Langthwaite was blown off several times. Doubtless, it was such unruly behaviour that excited the interest of a certain police officer who determined to square these ruffians up.

The confrontation took place at Langthwaite, in a 'High Noon' type of situation. On hearing the news of the policeman's arrival, the miners laid in ambush in small snickets within the village that would not be known to the unfortunate representative of law and order. As he advanced across the bridge, now famous because of the B.B.C. T.V. series, *All Creatures Great and Small*, half bobbins of dynamite came at him from all sides. Terrified, he hastily retreated back across the bridge, never to return, doubtless concluding that discretion was the better part of valour.

The poor relations between the constabulary and people of the hamlet continued on to the succeeding generation. A constable making a secret visit to the area hid his solid tyred bicycle beneath the bridge. Unhappily for him it was discovered, and with fiendish gusto the men cut off its tyres, ensuring the police officer a long walk home. In these days things are very different. Langthwaite can boast a mere half dozen permanent residents, some 26 of its properties being occupied for only part of the year.

Rich lead ore was found under Spanham Moor, and kept the Arkengarthdale miners in relative comfort whilst the mines in Swaledale languished. It is said that the deposits were so good that a miner could stand against the vein and lead would be visible to either side of his shoulders. Many of the miners would exit from the eastern end of the workings up the Hurr Gill Shaft. Late in the nineteenth century Big Willie Alderson of Eskeleth worked here. He was a mountain of a man, reputed to be seven feet tall. It is said of him that if the miner above him stood with his clogged feet upon his hands as he descended the ladder in the shaft, he took no notice. Despite his height, we are told, he could move remarkably well in the confined spaces below ground. He raised his fists but once against a man and knocked him into the mill slack (pond).

Inside an old Swaledale Coalmine.

Old Powder House Arkengarthdale, built at the turn of the 19th century.

He was an ardent patron of the Red Lion, but once he was in it he showed a marked reluctance to leave. The problem was that the landlady of the pub with her helpers could get him to the door but never through it. He would put his big arms around the door chiefs and refuse to move backward or forward. On one occasion, when displaying his customary stubbornness, he suddenly took it into his head to go and for good measure took the door with him as well. He displayed the same perversity when he visited villagers' cottages. Once he had crossed the threshold, it was not possible to get rid of him until he was ready to go. Because of this, no one wanted to admit him to their homes, but once he had put one foot through the door barring it from being closed he just had to be let it.

It is interesting that Big Willie is remembered for his stature and the gentleness that went with it, but I suspect that beneath the towering frame lurked a lonely man. Unlike many of his contemporaries he found no consolation in the Church, and his tendency to force himself upon unwilling hosts suggests a man who longed for company and perhaps lacked the support of family life. So many of his hours would be spent in the dark wet and cold of the mines, little wonder he loved the warmth of the Red Lion with its consoling ale that helped him to escape for but a brief span. His was a tragic end. After engaging in one of his customary drinking bouts during a severe winter, overcome with drowsiness, he lay down and fell asleep in the snow. The consequences for him were horrendous. When he wakened his hands were frost-bitten and gangrene had set in. The local physician was forced to operate without the aid of anaesthetic and both of Big Willie's hands were removed.

The shock occasioned by the operation and the psychological impact of the loss of his hands, the symbols of his strength, was too much for even his great frame to bear and departing this life, still only in his early 50's, we trust he found in death, the peace that had eluded him in life.

It was not just the miners, apparently, who were capable of noteworthy performances. Speaking of one of the more elevated members of the Swaledale community who greatly fancied the ladies, Fremie chuckled and said, "I've heard it said that people like him couldn't lie straight in bed, there was always something going on!"

Reference has already been made to the concern of the mining fraternity to protect ore that they had found, even to the extent of using mantraps. One old miner known to Fremie used to protect his interests by going to work at night. An old friend of his used to visit him regularly, and

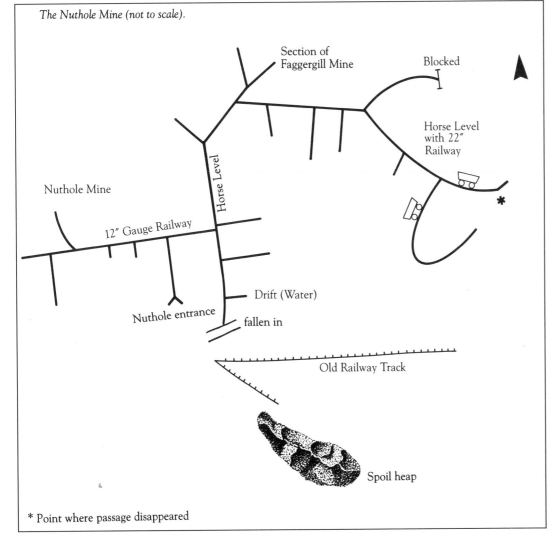

The Nuthole Mine (not to scale).

Section of Faggergill Mine

Blocked

Horse Level with 22" Railway

Nuthole Mine

Horse Level

12" Gauge Railway

Drift (Water)

Nuthole entrance

fallen in

Old Railway Track

Spoil heap

* Point where passage disappeared

Iron rails put in to support a weak roof. In front of the arch is a masons arch forming tool. Stang Level.

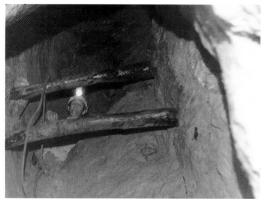

Small drift, Windeg Level.

Old hopper rising 55ft to vein, Windeg Level.

on the death of the old miner all the devout fellow wanted to remember his former friend by was his Bible. How thoroughly commendable, it was thought, until it was discovered that the Good Book was full of one pound notes!

So it was that an old miner gave me his impressions of an age that was long gone. The spirit of the time is best remembered by his recollection of John Tom Rutter, the last miner to live in Gunnerside. I recall John Tom myself, then an old man of ruddy countenance who used to purchase a strong pair of breeches each year from my wife's father, Clarkson Jackson, at the drapery shop in Silver Street, Reeth. He used to work in Arkengarthdale in the Punchard and Faggergill Mines. Each week he would take his food and dynamite supplies with him and walk up Gunnerside Gill, across the moor into Punchard Gill and on to his cottage at Whaw, a long and lonely trek as I can testify. Such was the spirit of the Old Man.

Although the main thrust of my interest has been in Swaledale, Arkengarthdale and its mines have neither escaped my notice or attention. The Moulds Level stands just off the road from Arkengarthdale to Low Row, and is easily recognised by its huge spoil heap. It has been possible to travel for several hundred yards in different directions within this mine, along Folly Vein, and to the edge of Stemple Vein. One of the outstanding features was a fine double arch, which does credit to the masons who built it. Nearby, strong beams used to shore up some of the workings, had been snapped like twigs by the enormous pressures exerted upon them.

During a visit to the Stang Level, which was partly flooded and could only be progressed in for about 100 yards, I noticed a five-inch coal seam in the wall. Where the level had collapsed, the miners had driven in iron rails to support a suspect roof, a technique that I had never seen before in Swaledale although I had noticed something similar in the Weardale Mines.

A young farmer had seen me emerge from the Stang Level, and told me that the Windeg Level further up the hill had been reopened. A large plastic pipe had been dropped on to the level, bypassing the blockage that sealed it. It was an interesting mine, containing several hoppers and a clay vein. Some writing in the clay suggested that a group from Earby in the County of Durham had reopened the mine, and their work seemed admirable. My brother was able to climb into a small drift some 15 to 20 feet above us. To achieve this we used some of the old stemples left in by the miners, and one of them held our combined weight. Their condition was remarkably good, since they must have been put in 80 to 100 years earlier.

The young farmer also mentioned Hurgill shaft, although at the time it was not clear to me where it was, as he had pointed rather vaguely out toward the open moor. I heard of it again through the late Joseph Harker, and after talking with 'Fremie' about Big Willie, I felt that I must find it.

After receiving some directions from a farmer, I set off with my wife Thelma into Hurr Gill. There had been some heavy recent snow falls but I was unable to dissuade my wife from making what I knew would be a difficult journey. The sun shone beautifully out of a crisp cloudless February sky, reflecting its brilliance amidst the snow clad hills. The going was heavy, snowdrifts abounded, and my wife continuously protested as she plunged through the thin crust of ice landing in various undignified postures.

I had been on this kind of search before. One can be within easy reach of a feature and still miss it. Further and further I penetrated the gill with no success. I was standing on a ridge of rubble that must surely be mining spoil, I reasoned, but I could not see the object of my endeavours. I was of a mind to press on but my wife begged me to turn back. Moving round to address her, I spotted the shaft down near the beck. It was very large. Strangely I had spotted the ring of rails marking it through my binoculars earlier, but had failed to interpret correctly what I had seen.

Later I returned to plumb the shaft, establishing that it dropped 90 feet before it bottomed, although doubtless originally it would be more like 120 feet. So this, I thought, is the place where Big Willie and many of his compatriots emerged from the mine after the day's work was done.

I stumbled upon Booze Wood Level by accident, but it proved to be a most interesting mine. It drove on to the Roger Vein, where there was ample evidence of lead. Progress could be made some 200 yards along the vein before it had fallen in, confronting us with a display of the most beautiful colours. This level was doubly interesting, for it cut through some good slate beds half way down the cross cut to the vein, where there were obvious indications of the slate mining that had taken place there up to the time of the First World War.

The mines that received my closest attention in Arkengarthdale were at Faggergill. The Nuthole was first brought to my notice by a friend and was so called because, after blasting out the vein, the miners noticed that the ore had the form of nuts. The level, driven in soft claylike rock, was very rickety and gave the appearance of a rabbit warren. In fact, on my second visit I had the most uncomfortable experience of getting lost. So real was my predicament that I prepared myself for a long wait until the fact that I was missing was discovered. However, using a process of elimination, I gradually found my way out of the labyrinth, emerging into the sunlight with little more than wounded pride to show for the experience.

A month or two later, I re-entered the mine with my son, intent upon mapping its general layout. About half a mile into it we picked out the dark silhouette of a miner's tub. Apart from the fact that it was missing one wheel it seemed to be in perfectly good order, and I tipped some water from it. We pressed on and rounded a bend. The level stretched out before us. It was a poor section, containing numerous rock falls. My son went on a short distance before me, climbing over two heaps of rock, and reported that there was water which he felt would come over his wellington boots. It was 1 p.m. so we decided not to proceed any further, expecting to explore this area at a later date, an intention that was never realised.

Old slate workings, Booze Wood Level.

This last experience represents one of the great mysteries of my wanderings in the mines. When I next returned to the Nuthole along with my brother and son, it was the clear intention to resume where we had left off on the previous occasion. To our astonishment, however, we were unable to find the passage and stone heaps that we had formerly seen, and there was no evidence of a blocked level. Instead we were confronted with a blank rock face resembling a forehead where we anticipated that the passage would be. As hard as we tried, we have never been able to explain these remarkably changed circumstances. During this visit, my brother discovered another tub about 100 yards into a drift sitting on the rails holding about 6 inches of water.

The Nuthole Mine, we are told, was driven during the period of the Stang and Cleasby Mines, which were formed in 1908. Narrow gauge railway was used for transport from the level, and a similar gauge railway runs away to the left in the mine. About 50 yards to the right, the narrow gauge is displaced by broadgauge, and this has led to the conclusion that the Nuthole joined up with Faggergill Mine, and if this is so the tubs we observed were located in the Faggergill Mine.

A tub sits on its rails in a drift, Faggergill Mine.

It is perfectly clear that miners would not transfer a load of ore or 'deads' from a horse to a hand tub for transport to the surface, and an examination of the Nuthole spoilheap confirms that the amount of debris deposited there is not anything like large enough to justify the multiplicity of workings underneath the edge of Cleasby Hill. In the mine there is a great network of horse level serviced by drifts in which small hand tubs were used. In all these tunnels we found no rises or hoppers and the generally horizontal workings that confronted us suggested 'flats'.

I began to believe that the Nuthole had joined up with the New Level, Faggergill No. 3, but after a discussion with 'Fremie', he convinced me that it was likely to have been the Old Level, Faggergill No. 1, which he said had wandered in many directions. He vehemently declared that the New Level went nowhere, raising echoes of the great controversy to which we have already alluded, the reverberations of which were already known to me.

Whilst he was in his 80's, I visited Williams Stones, son of Mathew Edward Stones, the celebrated water and metal diviner of Arkengarthdale. William Stones was able to demonstrate to me his own prowess with the hazel twig, and whilst in conversation with him he told me of an old miner who dreamed three nights in succession that if Faggergill New Level, which we know turned away to the left under the edge of Cleasby Hill, were driven straight forward, it would run into a rich strike of ore. Mathew Edward did not follow-up the old miner's dream until after the mining operations had ceased, but when he did, his son reported, the twig thumped upon his chest, and "He could not get off the ground for the ore".

A year or two later, after visiting Haggs Level, Fell End Mines, I ran across Mr. John Stubbs. He worked for 15 years himself in the Chert Mines on Fremington Edge, and his father George Stubbs had worked at the Punchard Coal Mine with William Scott for several years until about 1940, reminding us that there was a diversity of mining in Swaledale. This latter mine helped to sustain coal supplies, particularly during the long and bitter miners' strike of 1926. William Scott lived to the grand old age of 94, dying as late as 1977.

Black Chert was mined at the Hungry Hushes in Arkengarthdale, and Jake Stubbs, one of the miners, informed me that it was quite common for him and his colleagues to dig out lead whilst they were mining the chert. In fact he reported that five full bags of lead had been left behind when the mine was abandoned, and they are still there, buried in the bowels of the earth to this day.

It is interesting to note that the Chert Miners who were operating up to the early years of the Second World War, were using the same methods and techniques that had been passed down by the old lead miners. They still worked by candlelight, and until the last phase of the operation at Fremington, when mechanical boring techniques were introduced, worked with hammer and rock drill. They drilled their holes about three feet deep, positioned and primed their explosives, blasted, and retired to their lunch to allow the dust to settle. They were paid for the blocks of chert that they produced, and during a non-productive period were 'subbed' by their employer.

During my conversation with John Stubbs he repeated to me what William Stones had told me a year or two earlier. He further intriguingly added that William's brother Oliver had repeated the exercise carried out by his father, and marked the place where the reaction to the divining was most violent. Mr. Stubbs intimated that Oliver Stones, an old friend, had passed the information on how the place was to be found to him. So it would appear that the hills have not yet yielded up all of their secrets.

The Prys Level surface buildings, Shawbeck.

12

Farewell

In March 1982 I came to Gunnerside in search of a Ferguson Mowing Machine. I had not forgotten the important role played by that small tractor in the dale during my days as a minister. My quest finally led to the farm of Chris and Arnold Alderson, men slightly older than myself that I could well remember from my earlier acquaintance with the village. They were men of Ivlet, a small hamlet perched above the Swale to the west of Gunnerside. I was in luck that day, for Chris and Arnold were able to sell to me the type of mower for which I had been seeking. We reminisced about the old days, but I was shocked to hear that they were the sole survivors of the original inhabitants of the village and were due to leave within a year. This piece of information, combined with the fact that some thirty-six houses in Gunnerside were now used solely as holiday cottages, made me realise that the old close knit society that I had known nearly 30 years earlier no longer existed.

The villages of the dale were bounded by the steep moor sides, there was little travelling and the people largely entertained themselves. Many changes had occurred across the years. In the 18th Century, Swaledale was peopled with farmers who were part-time miners. During this period, the mines attracted men from places such as Cornwall and Germany. By the 19th Century, because families divided the land between their sons, Swaledale was now full of miners who were part time farmers. The 20th Century was to see the end of mining, although there was still a vivid memory of the Great Industry which was recalled with pride and affection.

There was no shortage of characters, they seemed to abound and their behaviour ensured that no one would ever suffer from boredom. A predecessor of mine, who had just started his ministry in the dale was asked to go out to a small village to bring comfort to a dying man and he braced himself as he prepared to meet him. As he entered the sick room the old fellow turned upon his bed and fixed the young minister with his eye. Referring to a local beauty he said, "Have you had your arm around Ada yet!"

Yet another predecessor spoke to me of the great men of prayer, many of them old miners, that he had ministered to in years gone by. With some humour, he recalled the old lady with whom he had lodged. Apparently, when he asked her if he could have a bath, she responded, "A bath, a bath! What do you want a bath for? I have never had a bath in my life!" A sentiment no doubt that would have been heartily approved by the people of her own generation.

There was a close bond between the men of Swaledale and their ministers, some of whom proved to be characters in their own right, like the one who used to start the day with a cold bath at the bottom of his garden. My old Superintendent Minister J. T. Lyon told me of a predecessor of his who, newly arrived in the dale, had planned himself in Arkengarthdale. It was winter, and the skies began to disgorge great flurries of snow. The congregation begged him to abandon the service so that he could get back to Reeth with his little car. He brushed aside and ignored all warnings, with the result that his car was trapped by the snow in Arkengarthdale for a whole week, to the obvious satisfaction of his flock.

I recall that one of the few people with whom I had a conversation about the mines during my sojourn in the dales was Mrs. Rhoda Hutchinson. She told me of how, as a young girl, she had worked on the dressing floor of an Arkengarthdale Mine, and of the decimation of the Methodist congregation when several families left the dale as the mines failed. This reminiscence is a reminder that across the years Swaledale has exported the skills and talents of hundreds of its people to the wider world to the impoverishment of itself.

During yet another visit to Arkengarthdale, I came upon Williams Hutchinson and Hird at Arkletown, expertly dissecting a pig that they had slaughtered. Having been insulated from the harsher aspects of life, I found the experience none too welcome. Although it was by no means common practice any longer, it was still then possible to find women who would make their own cheese and butter in the remoter parts of the dale, reminding us of how self-contained its people had been in former generations.

It was part of my duties when at Gunnerside to visit the Wesleyan School to give scripture lessons. It was a small school catering for children of mixed ages and superintended by Miss

Packman, who had given loyal service over many years. Now only the date stone remains, the school building having been destroyed by fire, perhaps symbolic of the end of an era.

The minister was also expected to go into the hayfield to help the members of his flock. I recall helping Jack Rutter, a son of George Rutter, the noted preacher of the previous generation. The weather was most beautiful, and without too much enthusiasm I repaired to the fields for an afternoon. We loaded the hay, which was transported away by horse and cart to a nearby byre. I can still remember swilling the dust down my throat with hot tea whilst we consumed large sandwiches sitting in a cow shed, the floor of which was liberally spattered with cow pats. From comments passed the following day, I don't think my parishioners had been too impressed by my performance, but then I can hardly blame them.

Whilst the chapel members approved of my youthful enthusiasm, they made sure that it was kept suitable in check. A fine band of young people attended the chapel, among them some pretty young girls. I lived in a small cottage of my own and decided that it would make a useful innovation to hold a meeting at my house instead of at the chapel. The idea seemed to go very well, and I was well pleased with the results. The young people were rather high spirited and must have made reference to the meeting on the school bus. Whilst the things they were reporting were harmless enough, the older people on the bus were somewhat disturbed at what they heard. I was soon left in no doubt that the senior members of the church were concerned by the idea of the cottage meetings, and rather reluctantly I felt obliged to take them back to the chapel.

There was never much fear of suffering from a swelled head in Gunnerside. At Christmas time, complete with piano accordion, the young people joined me in singing carols around the village. I think we all felt rather pleased with our efforts, but the following day one of my flock said, with typical Yorkshire bluntness, "I thought that was a poor sort of do last night." At the time I felt floored, but have enjoyed many a good laugh thinking about it since.

They were a lovable people, at times most irritating and on occasion totally immoveable. The Superintendent J. T. Lyon decided that there ought to be at least one week night meeting during the summer months. He therefore insisted on planning them, and I would race out to places like Keld only to find that I was the only person there. The locals were to be found in the hayfield, anywhere, but not in the chapel. As I reported to J.T. on the stubborness of the people, his face lit up, he chuckled and said, "The beggars".

I have referred already to the unreliability of the bush telegraph during my stay in the dale. The facts of the situation were too often blurred or totally lost through embellishment. I remember on one occasion I had gone to Reeth for the making of the Methodist Circuit Plan. I had spent an excellent day with J.T., spring was approaching and the hills were festooned with snow. That night I roared up to Gunnerside on my trusty B.S.A. motorcycle, without a care in the world until I reached Rowleth Bottom. Unbeknown to me the snow had been melting on the hills, and the road

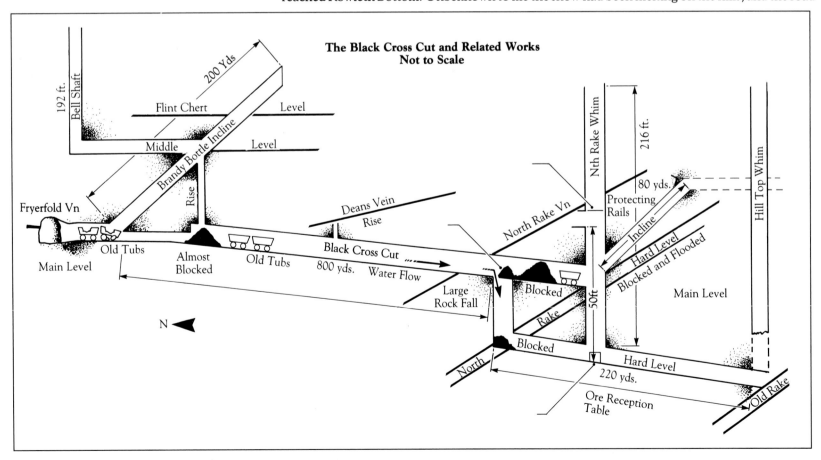

The Black Cross Cut and Related Works
Not to Scale

was awash with water. I was in the middle of it before I could take any action, and my motorcycle stuttered to an ignominious halt. I was ill-equipped for the experience and waded out of the water with my machine, having suffered nothing more than wet legs and feet. I was able to dry the contacts of my magneto, but not before some Gunnerside people came along in a car and learned of my mishap. The following day the village buzzed with the information that the young pa'son had come off at Rowleth Bottom. The gloss on the facts irritated me, although it was harmless enough. The trouble was, however, that this propensity to embellish events could and often did have more serious consequences.

Some months later another incident took place involving my motorcycle. Early one Sunday morning I was approaching Keld after visiting the Lake District. I rounded a bend to find another motorcycle parked in my path. Avoiding it, I was thrown against a wall and severely shaken. Half an hour or so later at Angram in the pouring rain I skidded at a bend and went in under a gate. If I had possessed a hammer then, I would have set about the bike, so great was my disgust. As it was, I was feeling rather ill and that afternoon was planning to preach at Hurst.

Hurst was a small village situated on the moors above Swaledale at an elevation of 1,200 feet. It appears to have come into existence in the seventeenth century as a direct consequence of the mining activity in the area, but now was but a shadow of its former self. I was in no fit state to set off on my own, and was accompanied by my neighbour Jim Calvert and Eric Herring, who kindly came to my aid.

The day was to be a chapter of misfortunes as we left Gunnerside in Jim's van. All went well until we began to climb Reels Head, where the vehicle proved to be too high geared to take the fierce hill and gave up. We passengers had to get out of it, and despite my ailing state, I had to assist Eric in pushing the van to get it going up the hill. We then had to struggle to the top of the wretched bank before we could ride again. On reaching the small chapel Jim, to his embarrassment, found that he had no collection, and between us after a 'whip round' we managed to muster the equivalent of the widow's mite! Falteringly I staggered through the service, and if my small congregation augmented by my two supporters gained any spiritual uplift from it, then there was a miracle wrought in Swaledale that day!

The people of Swaledale that I knew were hard working, generous with their substance and deeply influenced by a Christian outlook. There was a strong commitment to marriage and family life, to a degree that would be almost unattainable in these times. In this context, I cannot but recall the poor woman whose husband had been a perpetual trial to her. After his death the undertaker arrived at the cottage where the body lay. He expressed some doubt as to whether he could negotiate the narrow stairs with the coffin. The woman immediately shot off upstairs where there was the sound of thumping and disturbance. Soon she appeared at the head of the stairs with her husband's body wrapped loosely in a sheet which without ceremony she rapidly transported down the narrow stairs.

"There you are," she said to the dumbfounded undertaker, "you take him, because he has been a bad old beggar to me."

The humerous nature of this incident is obvious, but then so too is the tragedy. The words 'Til death us do part' in Swaledale in former times, meant exactly what they said.

There were strong pressures at work in the dale encouraging sexual probity, and this was manifest to me in the refusal of my flock to countenance my cottage meetings. For children to be born out of wedlock, of course, was a great disgrace, but an illegitimate child born within wedlock was invariably accepted. The marriage bond stood the strain and the child was given the full support of the family.

Whilst the people of Swaledale manifest many outstanding characteristics, inevitably they numbered among them those who refused to bow to the normally accepted standards. There was the miner who was said never to have done a day's work in his life, a harsh judgement I suspect, and the light-fingered among them; "Bye, if you left a bag on a wall, it would be gone with that one," or "He was a queer one," was said of another miner, "He'd pinch the dinner out of your box." Such failings along with instances of drunkenness and infidelity must be seen alongside a strong adherence to the Christian principles that had been fired among the dales people by Philip, the 4th Lord Wharton in the 17th, and John Wesley in the 18th centuries.

Lord Wharton set up a trust to distribute Bibles to the young people of Swaledale. It was a noteworthy achievement to receive such a prize, for to obtain it Psalms 1, 5, 15, 37, 101, 113 and 145 had to be recited from memory, along with other passages, before the minister. In 1827, at the age of ten, young James Clarkson, grandson of James Clarkson of Merrifield House, successfully repeated these psalms before Mr. Allison, and so it was recorded in his Wharton Bible. The repetition of these words of scripture doubtless burned themselves into the minds of the people and helps to explain their fortitude in the face of many adversities.

During John Wesley's visit to Swaledale in 1761, he wrote in his journal that the inhabitants were an earnest loving and simple people, although he was less impressed with their ministers.

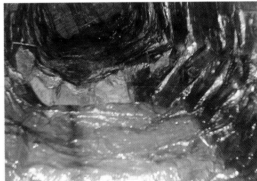

The horizontal walls and protective shield at Main Level, North Rake Whim.

One of the things that left the deepest impression upon me was the old style dales funeral at which I officiated in Muker. People came from all parts of the dale and death was faced head on, so to speak. It was the custom for all those who claimed relationship to the deceased to crowd into the room where the corpse lay in an open coffin. The minister offered a prayer, then all the mourners followed the body, which was laid on a small cart, in solemn procession to the chapel. A triumphant service was then held there, after which a great host processed to the burial ground where the committal took place. After these events we repaired to the village hall for an ample feast, and people who had not met in many a long day conversed earnestly the one with the other.

I remember attending a service at a small chapel, after which I was taken to a remote farm for supper. My hosts had a large family and we all sat around an equally large dining table. After grace had been said, we consumed an ample meal. The conversation was lively, and I could not but mark the strong bond that linked this family. It was Swaledale at its best. The hospitality proferred in the dale was second to none, and many a young World War II soldier experienced a warm welcome in a Swaledale home, and kept in touch with their former hosts for years after.

They told me that a young minister was urgently needed in the North East and sadly my short stay in Swaledale came to an abrupt end. I particularly missed playing football for Gunnerside with their enthusiastic supporters, who vocally cheered us on and were so liberal with their advice. "Come on, pa'son" they would cry, and should we fail to rise to their expectations they were always ready to question our parentage! Our sternest critic was Gregson Porter, who thundered his comments from the touchline. We alternated between heroes or rubbish, depending upon the state of play on the pitch. He never left us in any doubt about what he expected from us.

I climbed on to my motorcycle and drove out of the village for the last time in my official capacity and Gunnerside had said farewell to its young minister, for I was not to be replaced. As for me, I said farewell to more than I knew.

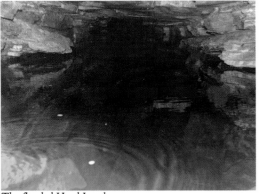

The flooded Hard Level.

My brother and I agreed to share one more week together in the mines, and the main object of our interest was to climb to the southern end of the Black Cross Cut. We believed it to be at the top of the shaft that we had found at the head of North Rake Vein Cross Cut. Our plan was to take a ladder with us so that we could ascend into the small drift at the side of the shaft, and from there, still using the ladder, we hoped to climb on to the top of the shaft.

The weather had been our enemy, rain having fallen continuously, flooding the levels. We had already made one abortive attempt to reach our destination, but had been driven back. For several days we delayed another attempt and we were rapidly running out of time. It was our last day, and on our way to the mine we noticed Knott's Level. We thought that it had been buried by Hard Level spoil and was no longer accessible. The miners in the 1850's had driven on to a vein about three feet thick that was plentiful in gangue minerals, but alas for them, barren of lead. Just further up the hill was another level on to the vein complex. The remains of an old building that once shrouded its entrance was still discernible.

As we noted the flooded state of Hard Level that day, our hearts sank. My brother favoured aborting the trip altogether, but I pressed for it to go on, having spent the previous evening up on the moor preparing for the enterprise. The water was bitter, but our ladder and equipment floated well. At the old air shaft the water was roaring through the narrow aperture there, and the thought of struggling through with our equipment caused me to blow up. I would have abandoned the project and turned back, but my brother was reluctant to do so now that he had been induced to start.

Deciding to go on, we wrestled our equipment through the small hole and without much further thought I pulled away at our load like a horse. With the cold eating into our bones we arrived at the Head, where we thankfully set up two candles and consumed some warm soup. We were already behind schedule and one of our lamps had failed. Grimly we pressed on up Old Rake Vein. Soon I was crawling on my hands and knees through six inches of water as we climbed over spoil that had been dumped in the level. Within 15 feet it had deepened to twelve inches, indicating that the debris beneath me was falling away. Again we plunged up to our chests in water and pressed on with scarcely a word, finally emerging from it at North Rake Vein Cross Cut.

Now we had to haul our equipment again, and it was slow work. Twenty yards into the cross cut my brother called a halt. In the dim light shed back by my lamp, his eagle eye had spotted something on the level wall. By adjusting the shadow we read,

The Old Man's Tombstone.

```
                    JW 1899
                       T
                        S
        GM                  TW
                  MS
                  GH
                       IP GC
                     oc 30
                     1799
```

For the first time we were taken out of ourselves and pondered the meaning of these marks. 1799 was the year of the Anti-Combination Acts, passed to suppress trade unions, although such legislation would have little meaning for the Old Man who operated in small partnerships of free bargainers. These were also the years of William Pitt the Younger and the French War. Beethoven composing his great music was a rising star on the continent of Europe. More importantly for the miners, the price of lead was about to soar, bringing comparative prosperity for the next 15 years.

North Rake Vein Cross Cut. The railway leaves the Reception Point on its way to the Old Rake.

The stepped incline at the southern end of Black Cross Cut.

Dismissing JW from our consideration, we were probably looking at the initials of the miners who drove the cross cut. Considering the experience of the miners who cut the Sir Francis, the date is fundamental in establishing that the Hard Level must have been started in about 1780, only two years after the infamous accident of 1778.

For years the driving force behind my endeavours had been to establish a link to James Clarkson who had miraculously escaped death in that year whilst the Spensley brothers perished. I had the feeling that my quest would be fulfilled if I could reach the foot of Hill Top Whim at Main Level. The decay in the mines would ensure that I would never achieve my objective, but here in this unlooked for place the link back across the generations was forged. Who were these men? We shall never know now, but they were contemporaries of James Clarkson and would have known him. One in fact might have been his own son George, who was born in 1779 and thus would be 20 years of age. The fact that GC was at the end of the list would suggest that he was the junior member of the team. Be that as it may, 21 years on the older miners among them would still carry in their minds the memory of the tragedy of 1778.

We could hear the roar of water.

"I hope that's not what I think it is," said my brother.

"No," I said optimistically, "It will be water coming out of North Rake."

As we made the shaft, my brother's worse fears were confirmed. Water was pouring from it and a close inspection made it clear that most of it was coming from the drift half way up the shaft which we hoped to explore. One thing was immediately clear, this drift was far more significant than we had ever imagined. We inspected North Rake and found the water there five feet higher than on our previous visit. The whole area had the appearance of an underground lake, and our deductions concerning this part of the mine had proved correct. Thousands of gallons of water were trapped in the North Rake Vein in Hard Level. It makes a controlled escape at the eastern end of the vein into Whites Cross Cut, ensuring the flow is unlikely to dry up even in the severest years of drought.

We now erected our ladder, standing it upon the ore collection point. Hesitatingly, I climbed through the pouring water up toward the drift. It was about 27 feet above the level. Carefully easing myself into it, I found that I was able to stand up to my full height. I immediately saw rails which quickly divided. Rounding a bend, I came upon a large iron tub and behind it a mass of debris had blocked the level. I quickly deduced that I was in the southern end of the Black Cross Cut. Turning around to come back, I saw ten feet above the cross cut stretching away before me at 30 degrees, an incline. My brother joined me and we lashed our ladder to some iron cleats that once carried a launder to syphon away the water that was now proving so troublesome.

With some help, I climbed into the incline. My brother followed, dislodging a large boulder that fell upon his head, but fortunately his helmet completely absorbed the blow. The incline was roughly stepped and was 80 yards long before it had fallen in.

It is difficult to understand the reason for the incline. Since it was above the Black Cross cut and was stepped, there seems to have been no intention to put in rails. Interestingly, it was driven from both ends, and seems to have been a walk way and probably had ventilation and drainage functions. Twice my light faded and came bright again, cruelly reminding us of our vulnerability. We saw an old clog print in some mud, and mused that we were probably the first men to walk the incline in 100 years. It was an astonishing and unexpected discovery, and we had no doubt that once again we were in the shadow of Frederick Hall, for it must have been his work.

An inspection of the top of the shaft appeared to reveal that it had been professionally blocked in by masons, but the large volume of water falling prevented us from seeing properly. There appeared to be a large number of rails thrown between a railway making entry impossible, but we felt sure that we were only 25 feet from Main Level.

We concluded that the shaft was a means of communication between the Main and Hard Levels, and ore as well as spoil was probably lowered down it to the reception point below. Hall later elected to start the Black Cross Cut from it, and the fact that he was obliged to pump water into it at the Fryerfold Vein, as we have noted, suggests that it was allowed to slope too steeply, so slightly misaligning with Main Level into which it ran at its northern end.

It was time to leave our enchanted world where we had endeavoured to ponder the past. We descended to Hard Level and immediately became aware of the cold and our miserable estate. And so it was that amidst the dark swirling waters of the North Rake, my compelling sense of mission began to ebb away.

After taking pictures of the all important date on the wall, which we christened the tombstone, we struggled up Old Rake Vein, shipping about half a gallon of water into our bag as we did so. A small candle stubbornly burned at the Head giving us some cheer as we made our way toward it. We fortified ourselves with the remains of our soup, and with little ceremony or regret gladly left. The journey for home was agonisingly slow, but at long last there was light at the end of the tunnel. Soaked and chilled to the marrow, we emerged into a wet and darkening evening.

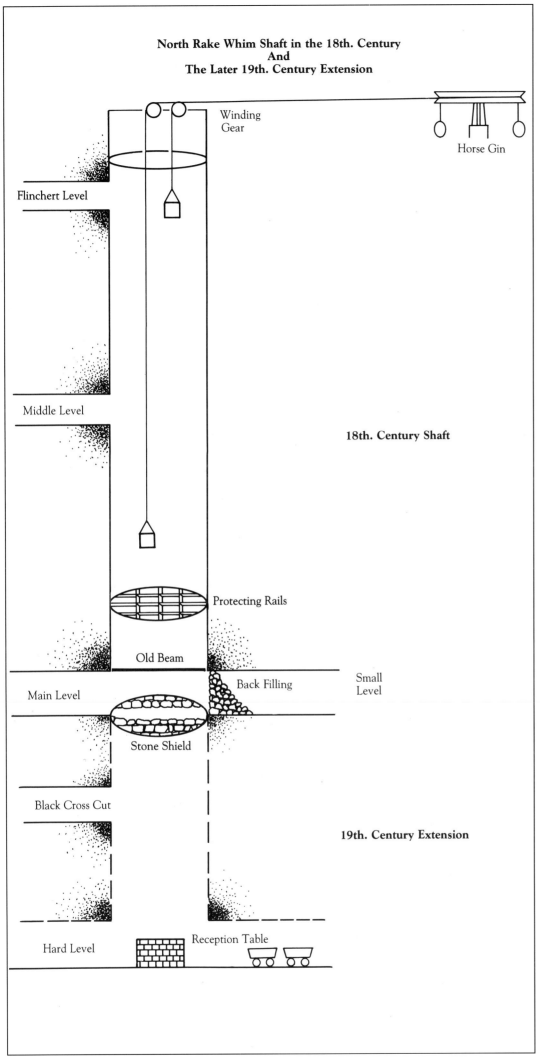

North Rake Whim Shaft in the 18th. Century
And
The Later 19th. Century Extension

Winding Gear

Horse Gin

Flinchert Level

Middle Level

18th. Century Shaft

Protecting Rails

Old Beam

Small Level

Main Level

Back Filling

Stone Shield

Black Cross Cut

19th. Century Extension

Hard Level

Reception Table

Water gushing from the Black Cross Cut into North Rake Whim.

With reluctance we agreed to return to the shaft when the mine was in a more benign mood, in order to obtain pictures and fully absorb what we had seen. When we were in the southern end of the Black Cross Cut, we could see what must have been Main Level at the top of the shaft. It came in from the north at one side. The rails that we had seen before were not stacked across the shaft as we had supposed with the purpose of blocking it. It was open and the rails were above the level and clearly intended to protect the miners working below. Opposite, the level had originally continued but was now walled in. It might have driven on to a nearby vein south of the North Rake Vein which we had noticed further east in Whites Cross Cut and was probably back filled as miners drove the shaft down.

We were not able to climb to the higher level and had to be content with the knowledge that at last we had seen it, after we had begun to wonder whether it existed. Later an examination of the photograph of the shaft taken from the Black Cross Cut sent me scurrying for my maps. I was astonished to find that tons of rock were piled on top of the rails, betraying the fact that the shaft went on up. We had already noticed, contrary to our previous belief, that it had been driven down to meet Hard Level, and now the maps made it clear that we were at the foot of North Rake Whim, a major shaft that went all the way to the surface, a distance of 216 feet. The rails positioned to afford safety to the miners had done their work. As the mines were vandalised, they kept the bottom of the shaft open, and it must be one of the few whose foot is not choked with rubble. An impression of it is appended. It was probably commenced in the 17th Century to work the lead in the upper strata. It was deepened and brought down below the Main Limestone during the course of the 18th Century, and was dropped on to the Hard Level in the early years of the 19th Century. The driving of the three major levels was largely the work of the 18th Century, although it continued in the 19th.

Once North Rake Whim had been identified with the aid of my maps, it was possible to draw some further conclusions about the Black Cross Cut. In 1821, Francis Gill had indicated that both the North Rake and Deans new Whim Shafts were in use at that time. By 1861 neither of them were considered worthy of mention by James A. Clarkson. The Black Cross Cut was driven through Deans Vein in about 1816, after which it was worked from the rise in the Cross Cut making Deans Vein Shaft largely redundant save perhaps for ventilation purposes. The shaft was probably connected directly to the Black Cross Cut, joining it at the rise 15 yards south of Deans Vein Hopper. The fact that James Clarkson finds no place for the North Rake Whim on his map suggests that the Black Cross Cut was used as a transport route until 1855, when mining ceased in the south eastern workings of Deans Vein.

North Rake Whim Shaft, left us with something of a mystery. An examination of the photograph taken inside the whim shaft clearly shows two horizontal drystone walls built out across it with no apparent support on one side. The question that we asked ourselves so many times was, "How did they do it?" The masons of Swaledale possessed the necessary skills to construct a horizontal dry stone wall. I had already discovered examples of the use of this technique in Priscilla

The Reception Point at the foot of North Rake Whim.

84

level. The secret of this type of construction apparently is to pack the stone tightly, allowing no play whatsoever.

The other question begging an answer is, "Why was such a construction necessary?" The North Rake Vein Cross Cut probably reached North Rake Vein in 1802, since it is about 200 yards from the miner's tombstone. The last 50 feet of the shaft would relate to this period since it would have supplied much needed ventilation for the Hard Level. The miners would lower kibbles of ore and spoil on to the stone table that had been constructed at the foot of the shaft, where they would be emptied into the tubs standing beside it. The old beam used for the early lifting and lowering operation is still visible in the shaft.

I suspect that the walls were built to give protection to the miners driving the shaft down to Hard level. The iron rails were probably put in later to protect the men lowering material from the Black Cross Cut down on to the stone table at the foot of the shaft.

Iron rails were not introduced into Old Gang until Hall took charge of mining operations in 1814, and the first of these were cast iron. The rails that we could see were almost certainly made of wrought iron and lifting equipment could easily have been attached to them.

Up to this time I tended to think of Hard Level as a mirror image of the Main Level above. It was now clear that it was no such thing. Before the Hard Level was completed the various mines were independent, being served by their own whim shaft, Hill Top, North Rake, Dolphin and Deans for entry, exit and haulage purposes. Hard Level introduced a different concept into lead mining in the Swaledale orefield as it began to join up the major veins by means of lengthy cross cuts.

Whilst in this place on my last visit, I tried to gain access to the major unblocked part of the Black Cross Cut to carry out a final inspection. It was two years since I had been here and I could scarcely believe what I saw. Tons of rock had fallen out of the roof and the way was barred. The strata here had been falling for many years and had buried the Hard Level in the western end of North Rake Vein, travelling west of the Black Cross Cut. The mine map clearly indicated the presence of such a level. The last trial in the western end of North Rake Vein took place here in 1863 when the level was pushed a further 80 yards beyond the old sump that had been sunk earlier in the century.

This great fall that I was observing reminded me of the sad nature of my task. The miners had all gone, and memory of them was rapidly fading. The very mines that they have left behind, tangible evidence of their decision making and struggles, are in their death throes as decay and destruction slowly but surely overwhelm them. I pondered the great jagged rocks above my head that barred the way, and as I did so I thought of the diminishing returns that rewarded my visits to the mines.

Rheumatism gnawed at my swollen right hand. The message that I was receiving was unambiguous. It was time to say "Farewell!"

Old tub in southern end of Black Cross Cut.